ML

HUNGER:

Man's Struggle to Feed Himself

HUNGER:
Man's Struggle to Feed Himself

BY JOHN SCOTT

Parents' Magazine Press • *New York*

To the late Henry A. Wallace

A friend and neighbor, pioneer of hybrid corn, long-time U.S. Secretary of Agriculture, and Vice President of the United States for four years. Wallace, a generation before most men, saw that good fortune and diligence had given the United States a golden opportunity to lead the world in growing food for the hungry and to help others learn to follow suit.

Background Books are concerned with the broad spectrum of people, places and events affecting the national and international scene. Written simply and clearly, they will engage the minds and interests of people living in a world of great change.

1516770

Contents

Photo Essays

Preface

LIKE MANY AMERICANS, I ate well as a child. I was vaguely conscious that others were not so fortunate, thanks in part to somewhat illogical admonitions from a frugal grandmother to "clean your plate. . . in India many little boys are hungry all the time." But I had no direct contact with starvation until I went to the Soviet Union in 1932 at the height of collectivization and concurrent famine. Most of the millions who perished during that period under Stalin were peasants whose grain was exported to buy machinery or sent to cities and construction sites to feed workers industrializing the country under the Five-Year Plan.

During and after World War II, I saw starvation in several countries—the result of the war's destruction of crops, reserves, and delivery and distribution machinery. Post war conditions improved rapidly in Western Europe as new varieties of grain and massive use of improved fertilizers and irrigation combined to produce spectacular crop yields there and in North America and Japan. By the late 1940's I saw the West Germans, gaunt and vacant-eyed on a starvation diet immediately after the war, stuffing themselves. I saw the fertile French countryside blossom with crops produced by a diminishing number of farmers aided by nearly a million tractors.

Only in Eastern Europe did food rationing drag on, but forced collectivization clearly seemed responsible; decollectivization in Yugoslavia and Poland led to sharp improvement in food production. In the rest of Eastern Europe and in the Soviet Union food production gradually improved, although the area showed no signs of being able to resume the massive grain exports that had helped feed Western Europe earlier in the century. The deficit in the world food balance, however, was made up by the fecundity of U.S., Canadian, and Australian fields and by spectacularly increased yields in traditionally heavy food-importing nations such as the United Kingdom and Japan.

The Specter of Famine Again

Then, in the early 1960's, reporting assignments took me around the periphery of China, and I learned that millions in that huge country were hungry. Too many Chinese were trying to make a living from too little land. Emaciated refugees crowded into Hong Kong as the Peking government abandoned industrialization projects to buy grain from Australia and Canada.

Then came two disastrous monsoons in India and Pakistan in 1965 and 1966, along with continued and increasing shortages of food in several parts of Latin America. I traveled widely in Asia and in such grim regions as Brazil's consistently hungry Northeast. I read predictions of incipient famine in much of the world and studied the agricultural and demographic statistics on which they were based. I marveled as India survived what otherwise would have been a massive famine in 1966, thanks to the importation of some 14 million tons of grain and other food from more than a score of nations. This effort, however, dangerously depleted food reserves in the "granary" countries—the U.S., Canada, Australia, Argentina, France —and, given the constant acceleration of population growth in the hungry developing countries of Asia, Africa, and Latin America, the future looked bleak indeed. Statisticians in the U.S. Department of Agriculture projected mass starvation by 1980 in much of the world. I studied with horror the Paddock brothers' suggestion that the U.S. aid program must apply the principle of *triage* and reduce soon or discontinue food shipments to those hungry countries which seem unable or unwilling to increase their own food production and reduce their birth rates.*

Projections Revised

The picture brightened substantially in 1967 and 1968. Improved weather and the results of cumulative efforts in the use of fertilizers, new seed varieties, and new irrigation projects produced a bumper crop in India, and good-to-excellent harvests in Pakistan, Mainland China and the Soviet Union. Such consistent importers of food as Iran

---

*This thesis was suggested by William and Paul Paddock in their book *Famine 1975! America's Decision: Who Will Survive?* Little Brown, 1968.

and the Philippines began to have surpluses. Economists revised their projections. United States farm officials stopped worrying about the depletion of grain reserves and began worrying about where surpluses would be sold. But in Rome the more broadly oriented experts of the United Nations Food and Agriculture Organization (FAO) remained basically apprehensive. The improved yields of 1967 and 1968 proved only what they knew already—that man need not starve.

The problem is not man's inability to produce food needed to nourish the six or eight billion human beings who will populate the earth by the end of the century. Clearly, the bounty of the earth's resources, harnessed by modern technology, is capable of producing the food men will require as far ahead as can be seen.

True, half the people in the world are undernourished, and tens of millions are suffering from acute malnutrition. True, had it not been for emergency aid, largely from the U.S., millions of Indians would have starved to death in 1966. And bad weather in India or China still might condemn scores of millions to starvation during any year. It is also true that in countries as richly endowed with fertile land as Brazil, children are dying from lack of protein.

Even in the U.S., hunger is shockingly present. More than ten million impoverished Americans, mostly in rural areas such as Appalachia and in the ghettos of the big cities, are now suffering from "poor" diet—defined as one that provides less than two-thirds of the prescribed allowances of one or more of nine essential nutrients. These include protein, calcium, and vitamins A and C. Some 280 of the nation's 3,100 countries are critical hunger areas, with infant death rates running to 15 per 1,000, twice the national average.

But these tragedies are unnecessary. They are manifestations of man's mismanagement of his environment rather than of any preordained and irrevocable imbalance between his numbers and his resources. The earth has everything necessary to grow and synthesize enough food to feed us all. The only absolute shortage we may face some day is space—room to sit or stand—and perhaps air to breathe. But this problem lies many generations ahead.

The task now lies in utilizing resources in an orderly manner to produce food and distribute it where needed. It is a problem of management—world economic management. It is the problem of channeling capital into plants to produce fertilizer to exploit the fecundity of newly developed varieties of rice and wheat and corn. It is the problem of water, of tailoring research to local conditions. It is the problem of motivating farmers to increase production and of educating consumers to eat fortified grain products, which will provide the only adequate diet that millions will be able to afford for some time to come. It is the problem of paying for the food the developing countries need, and at this point only the taxpayers of the developed countries are able to do so.

The task sounds simple enough, but it involves the application of newly acquired knowledge about soils, seeds, irrigation, transportation, storage, packaging, and merchandising, as well as what we know of nutrition, economics, sociology, and human motivations. It involves our ability to subordinate our personal or national interests to an over-all process of development with unity of purpose—within the framework of cultural, economic, educational, religious, and ideological diversity.

It is with these awesome tasks that this book deals.

Acknowledgments

To Julie Thordarson, my research assistant, my thanks for invaluable help in every phase of the preparation of this book.

To the many functionaries of the United Nations Food and Agriculture Organization in Rome and elsewhere, my gratitude for help in finding figures and evaluations and for making arrangements for me to see experts in many fields. I also owe thanks to officials and experts in the U.S. Department of Agriculture and in the various foundations.

Finally, to Time Inc. I owe thanks for permission to use material compiled for my earlier report to the publisher, *Hunger—Must We Starve?*

The Undernourished

1. *Malnutrition takes its toll.*

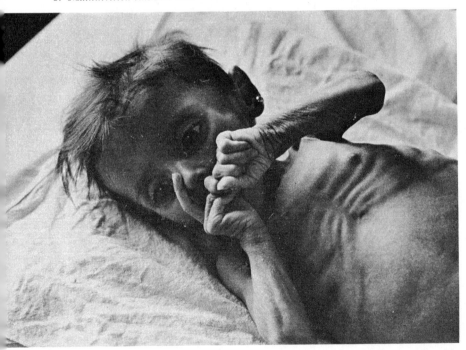

2. *Inadequate diet diminishes
the potential of children and
adults throughout the world.*

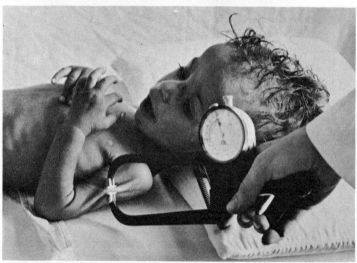

3. *Skin-fold caliper measures thinness of fat
beneath skin of a malnourished child's arm.*

1 Who Are the Hungry?

THE REVEREND THOMAS MALTHUS formulated a proposition in 1798 in his gloomy "Essay on the Principle of Population as it Affects the Future Improvement of Society." Throughout history, wrote Malthus, famine, war, and pestilence have tended to contain human population within the limits of its food resources. He claimed this was necessary because man's reproduction followed a geometric progression (2, 4, 8, 16) while he increased his production of food only by arithmetic progression (2, 4, 6, 8). He held that the massive famines in Bengal, which killed perhaps ten million people in 1769–70, were a warning that man was outrunning his food base and faced catastrophe.

Millions did starve to death in India and other densely populated areas in the eighteenth and nineteenth cen-

turies; nonetheless, the Malthusian thesis proved false—
at least at that time. For new lands in the Western Hemisphere, in Eastern Europe, and in Australia were secured
and put to the plow. Improved transport facilities on land
and sea, powered by the steam engine, moved the produce
to feed millions in the Old World, while other millions
migrated and prospered on the new lands.

Thus reprieved by extensive agriculture and the improved transportation born of the Industrial Revolution,
humanity continued to procreate at an ever-increasing rate.
Neither the famines that have plagued mankind nor the
wars that have scarred history from Malthus' time to ours
caused a ripple in the smooth and frightening majesty of
man's procreative curve (see Appendix I). Improved
medicine and sanitary engineering cut death rates so spectacularly that the loss of millions in wars and famines—
from Napoleon's day through World War I—was hardly
noticeable. Shiploads of grain and other food arrived regularly from new lands to feed the people of crowded Europe
better than ever before, while newly irrigated acres in Asia,
Africa, and their off-islands saved local millions from
hunger. Refrigeration technology kept pace with urban-
ization, bringing perishables to the teeming cities.

Although no new Malthus appeared in the 1920's,
scholars and statisticians had cause for apprehension. By
that time most of the virgin plains of the U.S. and Canada,
of Argentina and Uruguay, of Australia and New Zealand,
and of European Russia and southern Siberia—the empty
lands of a century earlier—had been parceled out and

ploughed. Improvidence and lack of conservation planning often had eroded vast areas to dusty unproductivity.
Remaining lands still unplanted seemed unusable because
of cold (as in northern Canada, Alaska, Greenland, northern Russia, and most of Siberia), or aridity (as in the
deserts of central Asia, North Africa, and Australia), or
inaccessibility (as in the rain forest valleys of the Congo
and the Amazon). Man seemed to have outlived the re-
prieve furnished by new lands. Again he faced starvation.

But once more ingenuity and imagination to modify his
environment came to man's rescue. The development of
manufactured fertilizers rich in nitrogen, phosphorus, and
potassium, the construction of huge dams and irrigation
projects, and the improvement of agricultural technology
brought about a kind of agricultural revolution in many
countries. Fertilizer production leaped ahead as a by-
product of the fossil fuel industry. Deep wells and hydraulic engineering turned deserts into blooming gardens
in the Southwest of the United States, in parts of the
Middle East, North Africa, Japan, China, India, and the
Andean countries. Concurrently, geneticists succeeded in
modifying plant varieties for specific soils and climates
and for intensive fertilization, allowing yields to double
and treble. A classic example of this development was
hybrid corn, widely adopted in the 1930's, which revolu-
tionized food production in the U.S. and in Mexico.

At the same time mechanization took much of the
drudgery out of farming. The farmer in the U.S., often
barely able to feed himself and his family in the eighteenth

century, fed not only himself but eight other people by the 1920's and by 1969 was producing enough for himself and 42 others. (Currently, with only 5 per cent of our people working the land, the country sells and gives away some 50 million tons of grain, powdered milk, cotton, and other produce every year.) The U.S. had more than met Malthus' challenge, and more than matched the geometric growth in population with added food.

To be sure, the U.S. was fortunate. A diligent population had inherited a vast supply of resources, untouched by war for more than a century. Moreover, the U.S. enjoyed the services and experience of many of the world's best scientific minds. Its economic system rewarded agricultural performance and stimulated effort. But the achievements of other countries, working with far fewer resources, were even more impressive. Western Europe and Japan, particularly, pulled ahead of the U.S. in the use of fertilizers and in yields.

Earth's Burgeoning Population

But while this new bounty benefited the world's developed countries, the planet's population was mushrooming. The human race doubled—from some 250 million to about 500 million—during the 16 centuries between Christ's day and the year 1600. It doubled again, to one billion, by about 1850. Only some 70 years were needed for it to double again to two billion by about 1920. Now, half a century later, it is approaching four billion and growing faster than ever. World population growth was about 2.2 per cent per century during the first millennium A.D. Now it is more than 2.2 per cent per year. Feeding the new millions is not the only problem. The burgeoning birth rate has changed the age structure of the population so that in some countries nearly half the population is under 16 years of age and unable to be fully productive, even if appropriate employment were available. Heavy capital investments are required for houses, schools, and industries—investments that the poorer countries cannot afford.

Indeed, population is increasing most rapidly in areas where it can least be afforded. South American growth of about 3 per cent a year is the world's highest for a whole continent, although individual countries such as Algeria, Morocco, Mexico, and Venezuela are growing annually at more than 3.5 per cent. The world's most populous countries are growing far faster than they can afford: Pakistan, about 3.2 per cent a year; India, 2.5 per cent; and China, perhaps 2 per cent, although no accurate statistics are available. Europe, on the other hand, is growing by only about 0.8 per cent a year, Japan by 0.9 per cent. In the Soviet Union the growth rate is down to about 1.4 per cent a year; in the U.S., about 1.6 per cent. Ironically, these countries could afford a far greater growth.

The rate of population increase for 34 very poor countries (per capita income less than $100 a year) averages 2.5 per cent; for 33 poor countries (per capita income

$100–$249), it is 2.2 per cent; for 39 middle-income countries ($250–$749), it is 1.9 per cent; and for 27 rich countries ($750–$3,000), it is 1.2 per cent.

The result of this imbalance is grim, to say the least. Whereas today only about half the human race is consistently undernourished, by the end of the century—if current trends continue—three-quarters of mankind will be in this condition.

As the hungry world becomes more populous, it has become better armed, due to the availability of new weapon systems (including nuclear rockets). Another factor contributing to the armament of hungry nations is the pressure on the world's arsenal nations such as the U.S. and the U.S.S.R. to sell or give away obsolescent weapons, in order to gain greater appropriations from their legislatures for new and even more destructive systems. This presents the world with frightening prospects: Before men allow themselves to starve, they may try to take food from those who have it.

I personally do not think this wretched cycle will run its course. Although the boomerang-shaped population curve has run smoothly for centuries, I believe it will be altered radically in the near future. This alteration will not result from the mass starvation predicted by Malthus. Reduced birth rates in Europe suggest that affluence and education lead to smaller families, thanks to unorganized and sometimes illegal measures for population control. Indeed, the Japanese—with an organized and government-subsidized effort—have done even more, reducing their birth rate from 34 per 1,000 in 1947 to 19 per 1,000 in 1967.

Only man, among the earth's living creatures, has the option to choose between the quality of life and its quantity—an option that should be exercised. Although this book is not primarily about population problems, it is germane to note that my studies have led me to believe that the acceleration of world population growth is likely to level off by about 1975—as indicated by my projection in Appendix I—then begin to decline toward a 1 per cent growth rate—which governments of such countries as India and Pakistan believe to be optimal for orderly economic and cultural development.

I have two reservations about this prognostication: Will the Vatican revise the attitude on population control expressed in Pope Paul's encyclical *Humanae Vitae,* released on July 29, 1968? (Without such a change, family planning will be difficult, particularly in highly religious areas such as Latin America where population control is most vitally needed.) And will Mainland China—recently so unpredictable on other subjects—exert major efforts to control its population growth, and give up its sometime expressed intention to swamp the rest of the world with its numbers?

But even if the world population growth rate does follow my projection, leveling off at about 2.5 per cent in the mid-1970's and then starting down, there are likely to be at least two billion more mouths to feed by the end of the century. Indeed, this is a conservative estimate.

Authoritative demographer Frank Notestein stated, at a conference of the American Assembly at Arden House of Columbia University in November 1968, that we must prepare to feed 6.9 billion people in the year 2000. Projections for the year 2000 made by the U.S. Department of Agriculture and by the U.N. put the figure at between six and eight billion.

Examine the Scoreboard

In this context let us examine the scoreboard in our present race against hunger. What are the prospects for keeping food production ahead of population growth in the years immediately ahead, pending the anticipated easing of population pressure by century's end? For this survey I drew heavily on statistics assembled by the Food and Agriculture Organization of the United Nations (FAO) in Rome and by the U.S. Department of Agriculture.

In 1965 world food production increased only slightly, and production in the world's less-developed countries, or LDC's, stood still. This meant that food availability per person in the hungry world went down by more than 2 per cent. Emergency aid usually arrived to alleviate starvation, but in most cases recipients were unable to pay for it, adding to the already heavy debt that burdened the living and the still unborn in most of those areas.

The 1966 crop was better, though principally in the developed countries. In the LDC's production increased over-all by only 1 per cent, and in Africa and Latin Amer-

ica there was a net decrease. These two lean years can-
celed the meager progress that had been achieved during
the previous decade. And lost ground is difficult to regain
because of the inexorable pressure of population growth.
To regain the per capita food production level of 1964,
the LDC's would have had to increase production by 7
per cent in 1967.

The lean years also reflected unfavorably on the LDC's
in general economic terms. Most of them depend on their
exports of primary commodities—coffee, jute, rubber,
cocoa, forest products, and minerals—for the foreign exchange needed to pay for imports. In 1966 the earnings
of the LDC's from agricultural exports fell by 2 per cent
in current prices and by 3 per cent in buying power of imported manufactured goods. At the same time food imports of these countries rose by 4 per cent.

Another result of these two years of low production
was the reduction of food reserves in the granary nations.
In the U.S. wheat carry-over at the end of 1966 was only
1,046,000 bushels. Canadian, Australian, and French reserves were likewise depleted by exports.

Looking at various regions in more detail, we see that
the 1966 crop in the Soviet Union and East Europe was
excellent, and food production increased by some 12 per
cent over 1965. In the Far East (excluding Mainland
China) it rose by 2 per cent over 1965, but by only 1 per
cent over 1964. In Oceania (Australia and New Zealand)
1966 brought a 16 per cent increase in food production

after a 6 per cent fall in 1965. In both Western Europe and North America food production increased from 3 to 4 per cent.

Viewing the world as a whole, grain production in 1966 was up by 10 per cent (wheat up 18 per cent), citrus fruit and jute production was up by 14 per cent, and the output of coffee, cotton, and wine declined. Meat production is estimated to have risen by about 5 per cent. But even with these achievements, the FAO noted soberly that the word "surpluses" could realistically be applied only to coffee, cotton, and sugar, and the United States revised its legislation with the "Food for Peace" act in 1966, anticipating chronic if not permanent world shortages of essential foods.

It is interesting that the use of commercial fertilizers by the LDC's increased by 11 per cent during 1966. But these countries still account for only 10 per cent of world consumption, although their combined population is about half that of the world. Tractor use also increased in the LDC's, but at the end of 1966 it was only 5 per cent of the world total.

A Look at 1967

The world's harvest was significantly increased in 1967, and since that is the latest year for which details are available, a more thorough examination is warranted. In 1967 the combined production of crops, livestock, fish, and forest products rose by about 3 per cent over 1966. For the LDC's the year was particularly gratifying, as it made up a portion of what they had lost during the previous lean years.

Viewing the 1967 crop region by region, we see that Western Europe had a comparatively good year, the crop being about 6 per cent above the 1966 level. Only in Finland, Norway, and Yugoslavia did production decline, largely because of bad weather. Grain production rose by as much as 30 per cent in some regions. Expansion of harvests was particularly great in Belgium, France, the United Kingdom, and Greece. Potato and sugar beet production was 5 per cent above 1966; fruit and vegetable production was up except in some regions of Italy and Spain, and wine production increased. An epidemic of hoof-and-mouth disease in England and an outbreak of swine fever in Italy caused declines in animal production in those two countries, but in the rest of the region meat production was good and dairy production rose more rapidly than demand, causing marketing problems and an increase in butter stocks.

Having had a record crop in 1966, it is not surprising that Eastern Europe and the U.S.S.R. harvested slightly less in 1967. In the U.S.S.R. alone, total food production rose by 1 per cent, although the grain crop of 147 million tons was well below the 1966 record of 171 million tons. This 1967 crop of grain was 7 per cent above the 1962–66 average, however, and made possible a substantial increase in Soviet reserves. Yet despite these two good grain crops, the Soviet Union continued to import annually nearly 300 million dollars worth of wheat from Canada, and to indicate by new orders that continued grain imports were anticipated. Soviet cotton production was unchanged in 1967, but rice was up by 25 per cent to about 900,000 tons. The potato and vegetable crops were good; meat and dairy production increased, although the number of animals declined—an indication of improved quality of livestock and of processing.

North American agricultural production in 1967 was 2 per cent above the 1966 level despite drought in parts of western Canada and a sharp decline in U.S. cotton production. The Canadian grain harvest—16 million tons—was down by 28 per cent from the exceptionally high 1966 level. Other crops also declined, with the exception of corn, which set a record at 1.9 million tons. The U.S. wheat crop was up by 18 per cent from 1966, feed grains by 11 per cent, and the soybean and rice crops set all-time records. The reduction in cotton production was in part the result of government programs designed to reduce surpluses. Milk production was unchanged, butter production increased by 10 per cent, and meat production rose slightly, to about 23 million metric tons.

In Australia, drought caused a reduction of agricultural production by some 11 per cent from the record level of 1966. Cotton production increased sharply, and for the first time in their history the Australians produced enough to meet their needs. New Zealand grain production rose by about 10 per cent. The production of wool was up by 5 per cent in New Zealand and 3 per cent in Australia. Milk production was unchanged in both countries, although the New Zealanders raised their butter production slightly.

In Latin America, the production of all foods rose by about 5 per cent in 1967. Argentina had an excellent grain harvest, and Brazil's coffee crop was up by 30 per cent. Production of sugar, cotton, and peanuts declined.

East Asia had a productive year, total agricultural production rising by about 6 per cent over the 1966 levels. Although good monsoons, in both India and Pakistan, were important, it should be noted that by 1967 new high-yielding varieties of grain had been introduced in 9 per cent of India's and Pakistan's effective acreage, and in 10 per cent of the Philippines'. India's total food grain crop—about 100 million tons—was a record and an increase of about one-third over the average of the previous two lean years. At 27 million tons, Pakistan's grain production was up by about 25 per cent. In the entire region (excluding Mainland China) rice production increased by 12 per cent above the 1966 level, though only 3 per cent above the 1964 level. Remembering that the population of this area is rising by perhaps 2 per cent a year, the per capita production of rice was still well below the 1964 level. Rice production in Indonesia, Malaysia, Thailand, and the Republic of Vietnam fell. Wheat production increased for the whole region, peanut production rose by 26 per cent, and sugar production was also sharply up.

Many experts—in Hong Kong, in Rome, and elsewhere—try to estimate agricultural and other production for Mainland China, which has published no such statistics for nearly a decade. Using their knowledge of 1967 weather and China's import figures, as well as information from refugees and travelers arriving in Hong Kong and statements of the Peking press, the FAO experts estimate that the 1967 food grain crop was excellent. They offer the figure of about 215 million tons and attribute the large crop mainly to favorable weather conditions. These experts estimate that Mainland China had a population of 780 million at the end of 1966. Other authorities in Hong Kong, however, put both figures substantially lower, estimating population at 700 million and food grain production (including potatoes and pulses converted to grain equivalents) at 175 million (metric) tons in 1965, 180 million tons in 1966, and 190 million tons in 1967.

In the Near East, agricultural production has increased fairly steadily during the past several years, and this trend continued in 1967, with an over-all increase of 4 per cent. Grain crops were up sharply in Iran, Syria, and Turkey— in Turkey partly because of the planting of 200,000 hectares* of high-yield wheats. Egypt's rice crop rose sharply, attributable at least partly to increased availability of water from the Aswan High Dam. The cotton crop was about the same as in 1966.

Africa's 6 per cent increase in agricultural production was the first in two years. The grain crop was excellent in South Africa, and good in Morocco, Algeria, and Kenya. Sugar production increased, and peanut produc-

---

* One hectare is equal to 2.41 acres.

tion rose spectacularly—100 per cent in South Africa and 50 per cent in Senegal, for an over-all rise of 12 per cent for the continent. The Nigerian war, on the other hand, was instrumental in the decline of palm nut and oil production, and cocoa production was off slightly. Coffee production rose by 10 per cent, matching the 1965 record level of 1.2 million metric tons; cotton production was unchanged, and tea and tobacco declined.

Appendix II provides more details on food tonnages, as well as comparisons with recent years.

Fish is an increasingly important source of human food, and a rather special industry, its main source being international waters. Fish production will be discussed in Chapter 8.

An Impressive Revolution in Asia

The most spectacular aspect of 1967 food production was, of course, the significant and surprising increases scored by two of the world's principal food problem countries—India and Pakistan—and several of their Asian neighbors.

Lester R. Brown, Special Assistant to former U.S. Secretary of Agriculture Orville Freeman, summarizes the situation in an article in the July 1968 *Foreign Affairs:* "As of mid-1968, both the food situation and food production prospects in Asia have changed almost beyond belief." He cites the Philippines, which in 1967 emerged as self-sufficient in rice for the first time since 1903; Iran, which became a net exporter of wheat; the spectacular 30 per cent increase in Pakistan's wheat crop; and India's 32 per cent food grain crop increase in 1967.

What has caused this "revolution" in Asian agriculture? First, several Asian governments have finally realized that agriculture must have top priorities. Ideas that were often associated with Harold Laski and the London School of Economics in the 1930's, that the development of new economies can best succeed by concentration on heavy industry and the public sector and that agriculture will take care of itself, have now been recognized by some as fallacious. Gunnar Myrdal, a long-time advocate of these attitudes, recognizes their fallacy in his recent book *Asian Drama,* based largely on the Indian experience. The Communist tendency to concentrate on industrialization and to solve agricultural problems by organizing peasants into collective farms has likewise been recognized as unrewarding on the basis of the poor performance of the Communist states in agriculture. First the Pakistani government, and now the Indian, have moved agricultural priorities to the top of the list, while still maintaining industrialization plans.

In India, for example, the agricultural development budget was increased by one-third for 1966-67. One-fifth of India's available foreign exchange is now being used for importation of fertilizer and raw materials for its manufacture. Fertilizer is the largest single item of Turkey's 1968 imports, and Pakistan is using twice as much as two years ago. Fertilizer consumption is expected to double again by 1970.

The rise of food prices and the resulting incentive to farmers to produce more is a second major factor in the agricultural revolution. This increase has been, of course, unpopular among food consumers in the cities. In the past, many governments have tried, often successfully, to maintain low food prices. Now it has been generally realized, however, that higher food prices constitute a major instrument for the increase of food production.

A further factor has been the cumulative effect of several years of patient work, often as a part of U.S. and other foreign aid, at building farm-to-market roads, promoting irrigation projects, and training agricultural specialists and technicians. During the past decade some 4,000 such Asian specialists have been trained by the combined efforts of the U.S. Agency for International Development, the U.S. Department of Agriculture, and the land-grant universities alone.

Still another element has been the building of several major fertilizer plants in Asian nations—South Korea, the Philippines, India, Iran, Malaysia, and Taiwan. Many of these factories were initially financed by the private sector of various developed countries in cooperation with local governments and industries. Now most are run by local organizations.

New plant varieties constitute one of the most spectacular factors in increasing food production. The Rockefeller and Ford foundations have been most important in financing the development of new Mexican wheats, rice varieties developed in the International Rice Research

Institute in Los Baños, near Manila in the Philippines, and other high-yield varieties of sorghum, millet, and corn. In 1964–65 only a few hundred acres in Asia were planted with these new kinds of seeds; by 1967–68, more than 20 million acres had been planted in a dozen Asian nations, and by the end of 1969, the area was expected to reach 40 million acres. Availability of these seeds from outside sources has saved the Asian developing countries years of work and immense efforts. In 1967 Pakistan, for example, imported 42,000 tons of high-yield wheat seed from Mexico and planted 1.5 million acres. In 1968 enough wheat seed was harvested to plant Pakistan's entire wheat acreage. India also imported the new seed, and in 1968 eight million acres of its area were in Mexican wheat. Turkey, starting late, in 1967 imported 21,000 tons of seed wheat, which are now paying off handsomely. These activities constitute, to use Lester Brown's words, "a massive infusion of a new technology at a nominal cost."

The new seed varieties require, of course, careful handling. The 120-day rice such as IR-8 yields three crops a year, so long as water and fertilizer are available, and there is labor power to prepare fields for the new crop and to harvest it. Where water is insufficient for three rice crops, sorghum or corn are useful substitutes, making possible combined yields as high as eight tons per acre per year. This contrasts favorably with the average of less than two tons of wheat per acre per year raised in Europe or the slightly more than two tons of rice in Japan. Now,

South and Southeast Asians can finally utilize their year-round growing season.

Naturally, this rapid development of Asian agriculture is putting pressure on the credit system as well as on transportation, marketing, and communications. From 1963 to 1968, for example, Pakistani farmers drilled 32,-000 tube wells in rice and wheat areas, and in India the number of wells is climbing rapidly also. These wells cost from $1,000 to $2,500 each, and as a rule they pay for themselves in the first two years. But they must be paid for, and these funds are difficult to obtain in countries where traditionally agricultural credit was obtainable only from the village money-lender at interest rates of from 20 per cent to 100 per cent per year. In many cases the profitability of the well has been so obvious to the farmer that previously hidden resources—such as ornamental gold and silver—have appeared to pay the bills, a most salutary phenomenon for all concerned, I believe.

In several parts of Asia, farmers have found that the fecundity of the new varieties and the profitability of double or triple cropping are so great that it is worthwhile to use hired tractors to prepare the land, rather than spend the time and effort needed to do the job by hand or with water buffalo. In Thailand, for example, in 1968 some 25,000 imported tractors plowed an estimated one-fourth of the total rice acreage. These machines were mostly operated by custom-hire entrepreneurs, a sort of Asian free-enterprise equivalent of the Soviet machine-tractor stations of the 1930's. The speeding up of the agricultural cycle made possible by the new varieties and mechanization has ameliorated seasonal rural unemployment, long one of the most wasteful and demoralizing aspects of the Asian scene. By the same token, this agricultural revolution is already producing new political forces —namely, a class of relatively affluent farmers now literate and articulate enough to seek to protect their interests.

This apparent breakthrough in Asian agriculture creates unavoidable problems, putting vast new demands on irrigation water, credit, transportation, storage, marketing. It also increases the need for foreign exchange to buy fertilizer, machinery, insecticides, and other items obtainable only from developed countries, while the food the farmers grow usually is sold for local currency. Thus, the Asian revolution will decrease the need for food aid from the granary nations, but it will increase the need for investment capital for the infrastructure—transport, communications, educational and political facilities—and private enterprises—fertilizer plants, grain elevators, tractors, and agricultural credit.

It may be that optimistic experts have over-reacted to the new developments in Asian agriculture, whose successes in 1967 and 1968 were at least partly the result of good weather. But it is clear that recent events have given rise to a wave of hope, enthusiasm, and even euphoria, which, if sustained, can be a major instrument for man in facing and solving the problem of hunger.

To summarize these introductory pages, the most important thing that can be concluded from recent developments in agriculture, particularly in the LDC's, is that the job ahead is difficult and complex. Feeding billions of people is a highly differentiated process, which requires the simultaneous presence of a large number of factors. The new varieties of grain produce well only if the fertilizer and water are available for double or triple cropping, if manpower is there at the proper time to plant and harvest, if transportation is available to take the crop to market, and if the returns are such that the farmer and everyone else along the line is motivated to work hard. Furthermore, producing enough food is only one aspect of development. It is essential that people be able to pay for the food; they must have employment opportunities, and that means industrialization and education—in short, rounded economic and cultural development.

We have surveyed the job to be done—to feed the world's population, currently mushrooming by about 70 million a year. Nearly half of the present world population is undernourished, particularly in proteins. Furthermore, we know from experience that as the percentage of young people in the population increases, the demand for food per capita increases. And as people become a bit more affluent, their tastes become more sophisticated and they demand more expensive foods, which means more food. Rather than nourishing themselves on rice, manioc, or millet with a bit of fish, they want eggs and meat and dairy products—which require more basic grain to produce.

Experts at the November 1968 American Assembly Conference in Harriman, N.Y., on overcoming world hunger concluded that food production in the LDC's must be increased by 4 per cent a year for the next generation.

Can this be done? Four per cent a year is twice the average rate at which food production has increased over the past 50 years in the fortunate U.S. To attempt to answer the question, let us take these complex factors of food production and study them one by one.

2 Mother Earth

WITHOUT THE SOIL, we could not live. Conversely, without life there would be no soil. Several billion years ago, soil was simply lifeless rock; it was ground into varied sizes by the action of the sea, glaciers, wind, and the eternally recurring freeze and thaw of seasonal change. This basic soil is classified as rock, boulders, stones, gravel, sand, and clay, depending on the size of the particles.

But in addition to its physical reduction, the earth's surface underwent a gradual chemical disintegration as the components of rock—silicates, oxides, salts, and other minerals—decomposed.

At some point in the distant past, three of these elements—carbon, oxygen, and hydrogen—were catalyzed by the energy of the sun and formed complex hydrocarbons, which began to grow. At first microscopic marine single-celled organisms, they then became more complex tiny plants, then living creatures. This long and fascinating story belongs properly to biology and botany and zoology. What interests us here is that as these first tiny living organisms established beachheads on land, they began to penetrate and modify the sand, gravel, and rock. They created what we now irreverently call "dirt"—our infinitely complex and varied soil.

A spoonful of ordinary dirt contains millions of microscopic bacteria and nearly as many minute spores and fungi. Each is living its life cycle, devouring other organisms and in turn being eaten—dying, decomposing, and in turn being reborn. In a shovelful of garden humus, many living organisms are visible to the naked eye—worms, beetles and other bugs, assorted larvae that in time will develop into insects, and perhaps a highly evolved vertebrate such as a mole, with circulatory and nervous systems nearly as sensitive and miraculous as our own.

The soil is highly varied in characteristics. In Hawaii and parts of the U.S. Southeast it is red; in North Dakota and along the coasts of New Zealand it is black; in the Sahara and other desert areas it is white. Such white soil seems lifeless until a few drops of rain cause it to burst forth with a myriad of wondrous desert flowers.

On most of the earth's surface the soil is in layers, or horizons. In river deltas, where fertile topsoils or humus have been deposited for millions of years, this layer is hundreds of feet thick. In some areas of the world, such as Connecticut, glaciers scraped away the soil so that outcroppings of rock are on the surface and often large boulders or even bedrock are not far below the surface.

Much of the earth's surface was forested. Some of it still is. Year after year, trees grow, shed their leaves, and eventually die and decay, eaten by the fungi, insects, and bacteria that live in the forest floor. As man cut down the trees, he modified the age-old cycle of growth and death and rebirth of living things. He also modified the landscape. It is said that some 2,000 years ago, when Spain was a Roman colony, monkeys could swing from limb to limb from Gibraltar to what is now Madrid. Today much of this land is a desert. When the trees were cut down, their roots could no longer retain moisture in the soil, and when it rained, flash floods often washed topsoil into river basins and the sea. A similar process occurred along the southern coast of the Mediterranean, which was forested until quite recently. The ancient Phoenicians grew fine crops along the fertile coastal plain; the Greeks and Romans used it as a source of grain and olives, watering their coastal farms with streams flowing from the wooded hills and mountains. Then the Bedouins came with their sheep and goats. Within a few generations the mature trees had been cut down or had died; the seedlings had been eaten; and the winter rains caused flash floods, which carried topsoil into the sea. Then came the sand, blown up from the desert. Formerly it was kept back by the forested mountains, like snowdrifts against a snow fence. But now the uninhibited sand has buried what only a few centuries ago were prosperous, teeming cities—such as

Lepcis Magna—sometimes to a depth of 20 or more feet.

Other catastrophes—not of man's making—beset the soil. Volcanoes erupted and buried entire valleys under thick layers of molten lava. Sometimes thousands of years were required before the lava cooled and decomposed and the first green shoots could push their way up, starting the process of making new soil. The millennial unrest of the earth's crust periodically raises ocean floors into high land, while other areas settle and gradually disappear into the sea, just as the coast of New Jersey is currently sinking into the sea at the rate of about one inch every year.

For man's purposes, of course, the soil is mainly important as a crop-growing medium with several functions. It is a repository of mineral and organic resources or nutrients, which plants need. It is a sponge that holds moisture until plants need it, and it is a physical substance in which the plant's roots can grow. As such, it must be soft enough for the roots to penetrate, but not so fluid as to afford no support, as is quicksand.

In addition to carbon, hydrogen, and oxygen, the elements that soil furnishes plants include (all usually in combination with other elements):

Nitrogen (N)	Iron (Fe)
Potassium (K)	Manganese (Mn)
Phosphorus (P)	Copper (Cu)
Calcium (Ca)	Boron (B)
Magnesium (Mg)	Zinc (Zn)
Sulfur (S)	

The elements in the column on the right are needed in only very small quantities, but nonetheless, their complete absence seriously limits the agricultural value of soil, since balance is another important soil characteristic. A soil rich in everything but iron is of little value for agriculture until the missing element is introduced. Moreover, a soil that has every important element but is so compact that air cannot penetrate will not grow good crops.

Nutrients are absorbed from the soil through the roots of the plant and play an essential part in the plant's growth and the development of the seeds, flowers, or fruits that are important sources of human food.

In addition to these elements, the roots also absorb organic compounds—complex hydrocarbons—produced by other plants or animals. In these compounds, which are present in large quantities in barnyard manure or in compost, the process of absorbing elements into organic matter has already been partly accomplished, and thus their presence saves the new plant time and effort.

Soil becomes depleted as crops are grown, particularly intensive crops such as corn or cotton, which man has bred and developed for his purposes. The soil can be rehabilitated by introducing artificial fertilizers rich in the needed elements. It can be rejuvenated by crop rotation, using plants that themselves enrich the soil; the leguminous vegetables, which have the ability to take nitrogen from the air and deposit it in small nodules on their roots are useful for this purpose. Also, the soil can be allowed to rest, to lie fallow, to rehabilitate it.

Some of the world's oldest agricultural lands lie in river valleys and deltas in which soil rejuvenation was carried out by nature. The Nile, for example, whose valley and deltas may be the site of man's earliest organized farming, in its annual floods carries thousands of tons of topsoil downstream—eroded from the upland sources of the river in Central and East Africa. This rich topsoil is deposited along the river banks and in the delta. In this connection some sophisticated critics believe that the Aswan High Dam may be an eventual disaster for Egypt's agriculture; it will virtually stop the annual flooding, and the nutrients that used to be deposited on the fellaheen's fields will settle uselessly to the floor of the new 600-mile-long lake.

The study of soils is far too complex and highly developed a science to take up here. However, one basic soil categorization—acid and alkaline—should be mentioned. Swamp peat soils are very acid, whereas arid desert soils tend to be alkaline. Most plants grow best in a slightly acid soil, but citrus trees require a highly acid soil. Preparation for a garden or lawn frequently involves "sweetening" the soil with lime in order to decrease its acidity. Good farmers constantly make tests and treat their land to maintain the proper degree of acidity. Today's Montagnards, in the highlands of South Vietnam, sweeten the soil with ash by burning over a piece of land, planting it, and reaping one harvest, then moving on.

Structure is another fundamental characteristic of soils.

For most purposes, soils should be porous to the degree that about 50 per cent of the total volume is solid matter. The other 50 per cent should be water and air, which the plants' roots need as much as mineral and organic nutrients. Air, of course, is generally available on the earth's surface. But water is not. The oceans, occupying two-thirds of the planet's surface, are too salty, too alkaline to be a healthful environment for most of the flora and fauna living on land. Thus, plants must depend for water on rainfall and the rivers and springs nourished by the rain.

Earlier in this chapter we mentioned that men first began to plant crops along rivers such as the Nile, Tigris, Indus, and Yangtze partly because of the rejuvenating effect of the annual river floods on the depleted soil. But a more important reason was that rivers furnished a constant source of water, both for drinking and other domestic uses, and for watering the crops. The importance of water to man in his efforts to feed himself has increased during the ten thousand years or so since he became a farmer. Thus we move now to the second basic factor important in producing food—water.

The Necessary Balance— Soil and Water

4. Erosion—the result
of loose surface soil
and excessive wind or rain.

5. *Terraces are one answer.*
Moroccan men construct
one near Rafsai and Tabouda
in the Western Riff, Morocco.

6. *Circular cultivation of chick*
peas, corn, and beans in the
Eastern Congo helps combat erosion.

7. *Terraces control water supply to rice paddies in the Philippines.*

8. *Turkish farmer learns to transplant pine trees as part of watershed reclamation project.*

9. *Texas farm uses both terraces and strip cropping to control erosion.*

10. *Egyptian farmer dips water from irrigation ditch to field.*

11. *Carrying water in Ecuador.*

12. *Persian water wheel powered by bullock in Guhugar village, India.*

13. *Water wheel— Egyptian style—in Oasis of Fayum.*

14. *Irrigation canal in Bali, East Indonesia.*

15. *Early canal system brings Himalayan water to India.*

16. *Diesel engine and pump with a 90-foot lift irrigates Arizona farmland.*

17. *The Aswan Dam has brought change to Egypt.*

18. *Israeli engineers fit sprayer irrigation system in Tel Aviv.*

19. *Hoover Dam in Colorado harnesses Colorado River for electric power and irrigation.*

3 When the Rains Don't Come

THROUGH THE EARTH'S miraculous water cycle, evaporation of sea water and its precipitation as rain play a major role in nourishing the diversity of life. But rain falls on the earth unevenly and with disquieting seasonal and annual variations. One-third of the earth's land surface is arid or semi-arid, another third is unusable for crops for other reasons. For every favored area such as the wheat lands of Washington state—where it rains regularly and in suitable quantities for wheat growing, thanks to prevailing winds and mountains—there are many other areas in which floods and droughts alternate to make agriculture a hazardous venture. From the earliest days of organized agriculture man has tried to induce rain by various kinds of magic. He has also sought to take advantage of other and more reliable sources of water—such as rivers and subsurface water.

Dams and ditches in river basins probably predated mankind by many millennia, as such diligent water animals as muskrats and beavers achieved astonishingly high levels of competence in hydraulic engineering. But man took the art further in river basins such as the Nile, the Tigris and Euphrates, the Indus, and the Yangtze; there is evidence that control of irrigation water was used by local ruling families or groups to enslave their less powerful countrymen. These early irrigation systems made possible greatly increased agricultural productivity and increased population. The larger population furnished manpower for armies and increased the power of the ancient kingdoms, which warred on each other as far back as Neolithic times.

The rivers that lent themselves to organized irrigation efforts were few, and man early discovered that excellent results could be achieved by the use of subsurface or ground water. In many arid areas, this water had been found seeping to the surface in oases or appearing as mountain or hillside springs. Naturally, this water came originally from rainfall—somewhere—but it was often carried hundreds of miles through porous rock or gravel, or sometimes in underground streams contained from below by impermeable strata of rock. The Phoenicians and Carthaginians, and later the Romans, built elaborate aqueducts to carry these waters by gravity flow from mountain sources to their teeming cities.

Estimates are that these underground water sources contain perhaps 3,000 times as much water as all the earth's rivers combined. It is available to the diligent digger, even under the most arid areas such as the Sahara Desert. Such water sources are now being utilized for irrigation in the deserts (now the blooming gardens) of California's Imperial Valley, and in the wheat lands of West Pakistan and India. But in antiquity, of course, well-drilling was a laborious hand operation, and so the ingenious *qanat* system was developed, probably by the Babylonians, and then vastly improved by the Persians. The leaders of that time, or perhaps their water-diviner-medicine-men would carefully examine the mountainsides surrounding arid but potentially fertile valleys. By observing the quality of plant life, and perhaps noting an occasional spring, and also by depending heavily on assorted divining rods or other supernatural devices, they tried to spot major sources of underground water. They then began to tunnel into the mountain, digging hallways two or three feet square, large enough for a man to work in a squatting position. Lighting their work with oil lamps, which also served to keep a straight line, and using primitive water levels to keep the grade even and slightly inclined, they burrowed deep into the mountain. Vertical shafts were used every hundred yards or so for ventilation and to remove the earth dug from the hill, which was winched up with primitive windlasses. Some of the *qanats* in Iran had shafts so deep that several relays of winches were used on different levels. Finally, if they were lucky, they struck an underground stream or spring. Then the water would flow by gravity down onto the fields, to the great benefit of all. In Iran, Syria, and many other parts of the ancient world, these *qanats* were often many miles long and irrigated hundreds of acres of fertile fields.

Other primitive systems of irrigation included the *challaf,* a huge wheel installed over a well, with buckets attached to its rim. Powered either by human workers or by camels or oxen walking around a turnstile, such a rig could lift hundreds of gallons of water daily a few feet to water fields. As recently as the 1940's, such systems were still in operation in Libya and Thailand. During the past years, however, they have been replaced by small locally made, one-lung gasoline engines. These may be seen chugging away, often protected from the hot sun by an umbrella and attended by a small boy or girl.

Still another simple device for irrigation was the ram, possibly an Egyptian invention, and still in occasional use today. The ram is simply a pipe with a valve that closes when water passes through it at more than a certain velocity. It is installed downstream from a dam or waterfall. Water flowing through the pipe gathers speed until the valve closes, at which point the momentum of the water drives it up through a vertical pipe and into an irrigation ditch or reservoir. Operating without supervision or maintenance, this simple device can lift water dozens of feet above a stream bed, day and night.

In the developed countries, of course, and in some of the LDC's, tube wells hundreds of feet deep are drilled with modern equipment, and deep-well pumps deliver thousands of gallons of water per hour.

The Industrial Revolution in the eighteenth century did away with the need for most of these ancient devices, as man became able to construct immense dams, backing up huge lakes. These waters were then fed by gravity through stone or cement-lined canals to fields sometimes as distant as several hundred miles. The Aswan High Dam in Egypt, recently completed in part with aid from the Soviet Union, will back up a lake some 600 miles long, extending into the Sudan. The lake will take eight to ten years to fill, depending on the rainfall in Central and East Africa, and it will increase Egypt's land under cultivation by some 30 per cent. During the ten years required to build the dam (at a cost of about $1 billion), Egypt's population will also have increased by some 30 per cent. Despite the heroic effort, therefore, Egypt will have made no progress in terms of the ratio of food production capacity to population.

Many large dams are now being built in areas as far apart as Siberia, Alaska, Australia, and the Middle East. They combine irrigation with hydroelectric power production, land conservation, and sometimes expanded river transport and fish production. Among the largest are the Bratsk project on the Yenisei River in Siberia, which will develop 4,500,000 kilowatts of power when completed, and the Aswan High Dam on the Nile, which is rated at 2,100,000 kilowatts—both the work of Soviet engineers and planners—although the British made the first tentative plans for the latter in 1912. The huge Bhakra Dam in India's Punjab was built with the aid of U.S. engineers—a feat that already has been instrumental in watering 6.5 million acres of previously arid land. One of the most spectacular projects is the Snowy Mountain complex in eastern Australia. Most of the water precipitated on Australia's mountain range runs off eastward across a fertile but rather narrow coastal plain. Only a small part of the moisture can be used for irrigation. On the other side of the mountains is the great arid Australian desert, currently used mainly for extensive animal husbandry, although the soil is capable, if irrigated, of producing fine crops of citrus fruits, cotton, and grain. The audacious Snowy Mountain Project, now nearing completion, will reverse rivers and make them flow inland onto the desert, irrigating millions of acres of new land.

All these grandiose hydraulic projects involve many different phases that must be coordinated if man is to make maximum use of the water available. Mountains and hills must be reforested, allowing roots to help retain moisture and prevent flash floods. Industries must be developed to make efficient use of the power produced, and transportation networks must be built to move the products—often aluminum or nitrogenous fertilizer or other products requiring large inputs of energy—to their markets. Measures must be taken to prevent industrial pollution of lakes and rivers. Thus far, such measures have not been adequate. Lake Erie is a classic example of how poorly this need has been met. Lake Baikal in Siberia is another. Ten years ago, its water was so pure it could be drunk by humans without danger. Now paper mills and other industries have polluted the lake and the rivers that flow from it, and the Soviet press is belatedly campaigning for antipollution measures.

Although some highly developed countries such as Switzerland have already built dams, aqueducts, and power plants to utilize almost all the mountain water potential, and although the water table under the cotton fields of western Arizona and elsewhere has fallen sharply, man has not yet begun to exhaust the water resources available from the world's lakes, rivers, and subsoil sources. Geologists believe, for example, that billions of acre-feet of water lie under the Sahara Desert in huge aquifers—enough water to irrigate millions of acres for centuries. The same is thought to be true of the arid deserts lying along the western coasts of the Americas from southern California to southern Chile.

But other sources of water already are being utilized. In tiny Kuwait, for example, it never rains, and no subsurface water has yet been found. But the country gets along well on desalinated sea water, relatively inexpensive at about 75¢ U.S. per thousand gallons—thanks to the local natural gas, which is virtually free. Using nuclear or perhaps solar energy, the cost of desalinating sea water is expected to fall by the end of the century to a price of five or ten cents per thousand gallons, which will make it profitable for use in irrigation.

Although meteorologists can barely predict the weather

with accuracy, we are all aware of their experiments with rain-making such as dropping iodine crystals into cloud formations. Experts predict that by the year 2000, rain-makers will be able to influence weather patterns by making some of the rain that now falls uselessly on the Indian Ocean shower instead the immense arid wastes of central Australia. In this, as in other respects, man's resources have still been barely touched, and Malthus' thesis of doom does not stand up under critical examination. Yet in many places today, children are starving because drought has killed the crops.

In India, late one afternoon in 1967 during the drought, I slowly drove through Bombay. Many districts in India's richest city were desperately poor. Hordes of ragged, sweating Indians faced evacuation from their huts and hovels because there was not enough water, even to drink.

I attended a mass rain prayer held in the docks area, in the auction hall of the cotton merchants association. Both the hall and the surrounding streets were crowded because the mills had been shut down for lack of water. The domed hall was about the size of a basketball court; a large dais had been erected in the middle of the floor, and around it lay heaping plates of food for the rain gods. A priest chanted a prayer, which blared throughout the hall and adjacent streets over a public address system. Several hundred men and a few women stood around, chiming in on the prayers. Many of the men, employees of the docks or of the cotton trading and processing industries, were Communists. "Communists want it to rain as much as the rest of us do," I was told, "so they come to pray too."

And then, as we left the ceremony—suddenly—it started to rain. Four inches in about three hours.

Revitalizing the Soil—
Fertilizer

20. *Fertilizer plant operated by T.V.A. at Wilson Dam.*

21. *Pouring fertilizer into hopper before spreading.*

4 Feeding the Soil

MAN BEGAN TO USE fertilizer on his early gardens and fruit trees long before he was able to record his experiences on clay tablets or the walls of caves. The discovery was probably accidental—perhaps someone buried a fish head under a hill of corn or beans and found that the hill was more productive than its neighbors. By the beginning of written history, organic matter, principally in the form of animal manure, was being used regularly to fertilize the fields. Homer mentions in passing the piles of manure "which the peasants were wont to put into the fields."

The use of human excrement as fertilizer also probably began very early, but it may have been discouraged for the very valid reason that it facilitated cyclical reproduction of microorganisms that cause and carry human diseases. But the systematic use of "night soil" as fertilizer has survived into this century in China and India. In the latter, one of the tasks assigned by tradition to the lowest caste—the "untouchables"—for centuries has been the removal of human waste for use as fertilizer on the fields.

Along with the development of modern chemistry has come greater ability to analyze soil. Man discovered what nutrients it contained, and how it could beneficially be enriched by the application of organic and mineral fertilizers. He learned that three elements important for plant growth—oxygen, hydrogen, and carbon—came not from the soil, but from water and air—aided in a complex chemistry by the sun's rays. Oxygen (O) makes up some 21 per cent of our air. Hydrogen (H) is present in water (H_2O), and carbon (C) is present in the atmosphere in large quantities, combined with oxygen as carbon dioxide (CO_2). Indeed, we early discovered something else of interest: Whereas animate creatures inhale oxygen to refresh their blood and exhale CO_2, the organisms of the plant kingdom do just the opposite—inhaling carbon dioxide and exhaling oxygen—maintaining the atmospheric balance vital to all living things. Man now may be threatening this balance with the widespread use of fossil fuels, which, in burning, consume oxygen and produce carbon monoxide (CO)—a poison for most living things. By absorbing still more of the oxygen so vital to human life, carbon monoxide becomes CO_2.

The three most important or primary nutrients that plants get from the soil are nitrogen (N), potassium (K), and phosphorus (P). These three elements are present in complex combinations with carbon, oxygen, and hydrogen in manure, in a fish head, or in a shovelful of compost, but the quantities are small. Many generations ago, man learned to add these three primary nutrients to soil more directly and more economically—in mineral or manufactured fertilizers. (The first fertilizer factory was built in England in the 1840's.)

The most important of these primary nutrients is nitrogen, a gas in its pure form, which makes up nearly 4 per cent by weight of most plants. There is nitrogen in the air, of course (about 78 per cent), and some plants—the leguminous vegetables—are able to absorb it. This is possible through the action of microbes that exist in nodules, or ball-shaped clumps, on the roots of such plants. The plants provide sugars for the microbes, which in turn supply all or at least part of the plant's nitrogen in soluble compound form. But most plants must seek their nitrogen from the soil in the form of nitrate (NO_3) or ammonium (NH_4).

To make up the nitrogen deficiency in soils, man learned to apply nitrogenous fertilizers. The most efficient yet developed is urea, $CO(NH_2)_2$, which is about 45 to 46 per cent nitrogen and is synthesized from carbon dioxide and ammonia. Energy usually comes from natural gas or one of the less valuable fractions of petroleum. Urea is most often used in the form of gray pellets, which are put on the fields by a spreader or duster. They are then broken down gradually by water, furnishing the soil with the needed nitrogen. Among other nitrogenous fertilizers are ammonium sulphate, $(NH_4)_2SO_4$, and ammonium nitrate, NH_4NO_3, byproducts of other industries.

The second primary nutrient often deficient in our soil is phosphorus, which makes up 0.1 to 0.4 per cent by weight of most plants. This element is usually applied to the soil in the form of phosphoric acid, P_2O_5—present in large quantities in many rock formations of the earth's crust. It need only be mined, crushed, and applied. The same is true for the third primary nutrient, potassium (K). This element is present as potassium oxide, K_2O, in rock formations, in a material known as potash. Several nations in the world are rich in phosphates and potash—the U.S., Chile, Morocco, India, China, the Soviet Union, and others. Both elements, but particularly potassium, are present in large quantities in sea water.

In addition to these three primary nutrients, most fertilizers also contain smaller quantities of secondary nutrients—calcium (Ca), manganese (Mn), magnesium (Mg), chlorine (Cl), iron (Fe), sulphur (S), and even more minute quantities of "trace elements," which plants also require. But because of the greater importance of the primary nutrients, fertilizers are usually measured by "nutrient content"—by weight of NKP. The same units are used to measure the cost of fertilizer and its use in units of weight per acre or per hectare.

Fertilizer production has become big business, and fertilizer use on large and efficient farms is complex and scientific. The process usually starts with soil analysis and blending of special fertilizers to meet specific needs. In twenty years, 1945–65, world fertilizer production rose from 7.5 million tons (of NKP) to 40 million tons. Fertilizer use, worldwide, is most uneven. The LDC's produce today less than 5 per cent of the world's supply, and they use only about 15 per cent of the world's total consumption.

Western Europe uses far more fertilizer per acre than does the United States. Among the reasons, U.S. agriculture traditionally has been more extensive than European, and the U.S. receives less rainfall than Europe, limiting the ability of the soil to absorb fertilizer. The most intensive use of fertilizer, not surprisingly, is to be found in Japan. There, more than 100 million people are now nearly self-sufficient in food, although the total area of the archipelago is less than that of California, and most of it is mountains and rocks. In 1965–66 the Japanese used 319 kilograms of fertilizer per hectare, compared with 130 in Europe and 52 in North America. The Soviet Union and Eastern Europe made even less use of fertilizer—only 36 kilograms per hectare. For the less-developed countries, the figures are shocking: 16 kilograms for Latin America, 12 for Asia, two for Africa.

The effectiveness of fertilizer in increasing yields is well known and almost universally accepted. Indeed, it is not superstitious farmers in the LDC's who are reluctant to use manufactured fertilizers. Even in the most remote parts of India, Pakistan, and Brazil, most farmers now want fertilizer. Ironically, more formally educated people in London, New York, or Los Angeles insist that "chemical fertilizer" is not "natural," that it is harmful and should not be used. The fact is that any material is "chemical" in that it has a chemical formula. A molecule of ammonia taken from manure is exactly the same in structure and other respects as an ammonia molecule fixed in a chemical plant with the use of natural gas and air.

Spectacular yield increases frequently are achieved for certain crops as a result of using various fertilizers. The thrust of this knowledge and experience is now widely accepted, as is the other side of the coin: Highly developed and specialized crops remove substantial nutrients from the soil every year. For example, a hectare of land planted with potatoes will produce under good conditions 20,000 kilograms of potatoes, but it will lose 140 kilograms of nitrogen and 190 kilograms of potassium oxide in the process. A hectare of land can produce 25,000 kilograms of sugarcane, but in so doing it loses 30 kilograms of nitrogen and 60 kilograms of potassium oxide. Corn and cotton are both highly debilitating to the soil, and the harvesting of such intensive crops without replacing the nutrients leads rapidly to soil exhaustion.

Farmers want fertilizer. They know that it will increase their yields and their incomes substantially, but the bitter economic fact is that in too many cases they cannot afford to pay for it.

At a large sugar plantation near Recife in northeastern Brazil, where farmers used fertilizers imported from Germany and the United Kingdom with excellent results, the plantation manager was nevertheless unhappy. He had 7,000 hectares in cane, but he fertilized only about 3,000, using 600 kilograms of ammonium sulphate, 130 kilograms of potash, and 120 kilograms of phosphate per hectare, the minimum recommended level. The cost of fertilizing one hectare is about 35 U.S. dollars. Application costs are negligible, and sugar yields are increased by about 120 dollars per hectare—a threefold return on the money in a year. But the manager could not get the credit to buy the fertilizer he needed to fertilize all his land. He was already in debt and was paying a minimum of 25 per cent interest. There just wasn't any more money within his reach.

If a large plantation manager was in this position, imagine the plight of the small farmer with no contacts and limited technical knowledge and experience. He uses little or no fertilizer, because he cannot afford to buy it, and the economic framework of his existence gives him no opportunities to borrow.

This appears as one of the most dreadful anomalies in our contemporary world. Machinery capable of producing some two million tons of fertilizer is idle today because overexpansion and overproduction forced prices below the point at which the chemical companies can meet their costs, let alone make a profit. From 1963 to 1968, U.S. companies spent some $4 billion—much of it borrowed from banks and insurance companies—opening potash and phosphate mines and building plants and transport facilities in the LDC's. The companies knew that the imbalance between the world's population growth rate

of more than 2 per cent a year, and its demand for food—
increasing by about 4 per cent a year—would have to be
met with the aid of massive inputs of fertilizer. The use
of fertilizer would benefit the countries as well as the
companies.

An official of Hercules, Incorporated, a large U.S. fertilizer company, makes the following estimate of the
economics of the response of Mexipak wheat to urea
fertilization in Pakistan. About ten pounds of wheat
are produced for every pound of fertilizer used. One metric
ton of urea increases the yield of wheat by about 370
bushels, and thus a urea plant producing 345,000 metric
tons a year would be equivalent to an increase of over
125 million bushels of wheat a year (about 3.5 million
metric tons). At today's prices, this would mean saving
about $25 million yearly in foreign exchange (replacing
imports of fertilizer) and would generate an increased
value of grain inside Pakistan of around $300 million a
year.

How will we explain this lethal human irony to future
generations? Put more poetically by Edwin Markham in
his mighty poem *The Man with the Hoe:*

How will the Future reckon with this man?
How answer his brute question in that hour
When whirlwinds of rebellion shake all shores?

5 Seeds of Life

As we have already noted, one of the most vital factors contributing to the agricultural revolution in Asia and to the improved world food picture is the development of new varieties of food grain. Although plant-breeding efforts have been going on for many centuries, it is largely in the twentieth century that dramatic progress has been made in developing varieties that increase yields.

The development of hybrid corn in the U.S. is an early example of genetic progress of this kind. Developed in about 1917, hybrid corn was not planted to any significant extent until the 1930's. Between that time and the mid-1960's, it is estimated that American corn production increased by 100 per cent—on 33 per cent fewer acres. Average per acre yield increased from 20.5 bushels to 67.3 bushels during that period. The hybrid strains were bred to fit the characteristics of their intended regions of planting; provision was made for variations in the period of maturation, adaptation to regional humidity levels, special resistance to regional diseases, tight- or loose-fitting husk, weaker or stronger stalk, shorter or taller plant, oil content—plus an infinite number of other factors. It is significant that it took the relatively progressive U.S. farmer two or three decades to accept hybrid seed corn and learn to use it effectively.

New varieties of rice, wheat, sorghum, and other grains were subsequently developed, and their acceptance was effected far more quickly. The need for more food in the rice- and wheat-eating nations was critical, and the developed countries and international organizations provided economic aid and set up numerous pilot projects to convince the farmer of the merits of the new seeds.

The most important of the new varieties of wheat were developed at the International Maize and Wheat Improvement Center in Mexico, sponsored by the Rockefeller Foundation. These new seeds were responsible for changing Mexico from a sizable net importer of grain to a net exporter: As recently as the early 1950's an average of 315,000 tons was being *imported* annually—about half as much as Mexico produced. In 1967 Mexico *exported* 147,-977 tons. Mexico's total cereal production trebled in just 20 years.

A significant characteristic of Mexican wheat is that it is short statured and stiff. The increased use of nitrogen fertilizer produced heads of grain so heavy that the stalk could not support the weight, and the plant fell over (called "lodging"). The new wheat, however, is capable of using 80 pounds of fertilizer per acre without lodging. In addition, it is not photosensitive and matures in a certain period, regardless of length of day. Some varieties have a relatively short period of maturation, permitting double cropping or sometimes even triple cropping.

In the early 1960's Pakistan became vitally interested in the new strains of wheat developed in Mexico, and scientists set to work crossing dwarf Mexican wheat with taller indigenous varieties. Several new types were developed, the most successful of which are "Mexipak" and "Indus 66." Amber in color and bland in taste (as is preferred by the local people), the new varieties are resistant to local diseases and insects, in addition to being superior in nutritional value, more responsive to nitrogen fertilizers, and higher in yield.

The first harvest of Mexican wheat seed yielded an average of 1,600 kilograms per acre. On some farms the yield was as high as 3,000 kilograms per acre—six times the yield from the best local strain. Success of the new wheat seeds has been so great that Pakistan, which is normally plagued with a wheat deficit of some two million tons a year, foresees self-sufficiency in that commodity in the immediate future.

In India, too, the dwarf Mexican variety was the hero of a wheat revolution. As had been the case in Pakistan, researchers in agricultural universities and other institutes began crossing local varieties with the Mexican wheat. They took the most promising of the Mexican dwarfs— Sonora 64—and subjected it to ionizing radiation. The result was a mutant with amber grains, which they called Sharbati Sonora. In the new seeds there are two genes for dwarfing; to keep height down, two successive mutations have been bred into the seed. Under only average conditions Sharbati Sonora yields 125 maunds (about five tons) per hectare, compared with 25 maunds per hectare for India's traditional wheat. Furthermore, it contains 16.5 per cent protein, more than the 14 per cent of its Mexican parents and far more than the 9 per cent of ordinary wheat.

Scientists are now developing three-gene dwarfs, even more resistant to lodging and with vertical angular leaves, able to capture more of India's large amounts of solar energy. The first of the new wheats was grown in India in 1963, and it is now likely that the traditional tall-stalked varieties will be completely replaced. In 1968 nearly 17 million tons of wheat were harvested, against the previous record of 12 million tons in 1964. Prime Minister Indira Gandhi has asserted that India would be self-sufficient in wheat by 1971, although foreign experts have their fingers crossed because of the vulnerability of Indian agriculture to bad monsoons, such as those of 1965 and 1966.

Important, too, is the progress made with new varieties of rice. Two of every three Asians depend on rice for the bulk of their food supply, the average annual consumption of rice per Asian being 200 to 400 pounds. In 1966 former U.S. foreign aid consultant Paul Deutschman estimated that an additional 10,000,000 tons of rice would be needed yearly—just to feed Asia's burgeoning population at its then inadequate level.

With this challenge before them, scientists at the International Rice Research Institute (IRRI) began work on new strains. Founded in 1962 at Los Baños, near Manila in the Philippines, the institute is managed by the Rockefeller Foundation. Its funds are provided on a 50-50 basis by that group and the Ford Foundation.

The function of IRRI is basically educational. It investigates every aspect of rice—varieties, pathology, fertilizers, economics—and provides an international training center for young scientists from all rice-producing countries, particularly those in Southeast Asia.

In late 1966 the scientists at the institute announced the hybridization of a new variety of rice called IR-8. Promptly dubbed "miracle rice," it was tough and hardy, would grow almost anywhere, yielded from two to six times as much as other strains, and gave hope that Asia might overcome its consistent rice shortage.

Numerous were the problems associated with the new rice, however. It proved vulnerable to plant viruses and insects and took too long to mature. Most serious, perhaps, was the fact that the hard, dry grains broke in milling and their texture was unpleasant to the tongue. Scientists at IRRI continued to work with IR-8, crossing it with other strains having the qualities they desired. The results thus far have been encouraging: Improved IR-8 varieties ripen in 120 to 125 days, compared to 150 to 180 days for the traditional types. They are rather insensitive to light and can be sown in any season, given suitable temperature and water supply. In some areas two or even three crops may be harvested each year.

After only three seasons, more than half the farmers in

the Philippines' key rice-producing Laguna Province switched to miracle rice, more than doubling yields and profits. IR-8 is now grown on only 10 per cent of Philippines rice land, yet in 18 months it made the Philippines— for the first time in modern history—self-sufficient in rice.

Improved IR-8 is rapidly becoming the standard rice of Southeast Asia. Its higher yields and larger profits added $300 million to the incomes of Southeast Asian farmers in 1968. India will more than double its IR-8 plantings to two million acres this season. Burma hopes to go from 80,000 acres to 800,000.

IR-8 has been planted in South Vietnam since 1966, initially smuggled in and secretly sown by enthusiastic U.S. agricultural advisers. South Vietnam was once a rice exporter, but the chaos of the war had necessitated importing 600,000 tons of U.S. and Thai rice yearly. Yields of IR-8 have proven so much greater than the traditional strains, however, that there is hope for a return to self-sufficiency. Some Vietnamese farmers have come to refer to IR-8 as "Honda rice"—additional profits are often enough to let them buy a motorcycle.

As agricultural expert Lester Brown says, the new cereal varieties are "so superior to traditional varieties and so dramatic in their impact that they are becoming 'engines of change' wherever used. They may be to the agricultural revolution in Asia what the steam engine was to the Industrial Revolution in Europe."

The Corn Story

22. *Closeup of hybrid ears.*

23. *Preparing the land in Peru.*

24. *Plowing in rural area of Turkey.*

25. *Planting in the U.S. Metal chains bury the seeds.*

26. *Field corn "in tassle."*

27. *Storing maize in trees in Nepal.*

28. *Moroccan farmer displays results of using fertilizer to grow maize.*

29. *Picking out the best at Sumatran market, Indonesia.*

30. *Drying corn in Sumatra.*

What Price, Rice?

31. *Closeup of Philippine variety of rice, Itan.*

32. *International Rice Research Institute experiments determine which rice can best resist the virus-carrying brown plant hopper.*

33. *Preparing the pannicle of IR-8 type rice to cross with another variety.*

34. *Rice growing in the fields.*

35. *Vietnamese farmers work the land.*

36. Rice field near
Worosobo, Java-Indonesia.

37. Threashing paddy from
an experimental plot in
Caspian area of Iran.

38. Irrigating rice fields
in Brazil.

39. Ceylonese rice workers.

40. *Drying Formosan rice starch in the sun.*

41. *Towel and gauntlets
protect Taiwanese girls
turning rice starch as it dries.*

The Wonder of Wheat

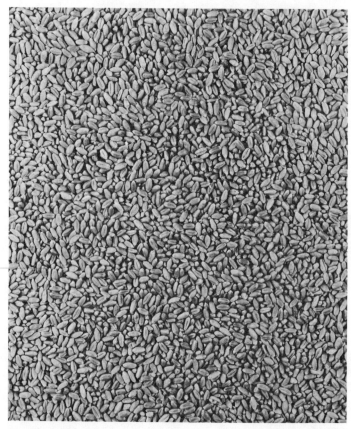

42. *Closeup of wheat kernels.*

43. *Frightening birds away from Ethiopian millet fields. Method used also in wheat fields.*

44. *Examining experimental wheat field in Ecuador.*

45. *Hand reaping in Sakha, Egypt.*

46. *Windrowing wheat in California.*

47. *Bladed wheels chop Turkish wheat for market.*

48. *Near Jajce, Yugoslavia, river powers grain mill.*

49. *Wheat harvested in Russia.*

50. *Treading wheat outside Bethlehem, Israel.*

51. *Bagging wheat from abroad during India's 1966 food emergency.*

52. *Grain hand-cleaned at market in India.*

6 Battle of the Pests

CAREFUL ESTIMATES SUGGEST that 20 to 30 per cent of all the food that man produces for his own consumption is eaten instead by assorted pests—bacteria, fungi, protozoa, nematodes, insects, birds, rodents. In addition to this loss, large quantities of land area, water, and soil nutrients nourish weeds, often hardier than the crops they encroach upon, but of no use to man. Furthermore, as man develops his agriculture with intensive crops, the pests living on these crops also increase in number. Rats, for example, tend to reproduce explosively in a good apple orchard. All this means that agricultural improvements, if they are to be effective, must be accompanied by pest control.

Man has developed several ways to destroy, or at least control, pests. The simplest and most ancient method was

manual—rats were caught either by hand or in traps and
killed. Noxious bugs and beetles were picked from plants
by hand and destroyed. The fly-swatter may be one of
man's most ancient tools. Weeds were pulled out by hand
or with cultivators.

Then came pesticides. They were poisons to kill pests,
insects, and parasitic microorganisms, as well as rats, foxes,
and birds. Often the pesticides were not selective and
killed anything with which they came into contact. Applied manually or with sprayers or dusters, most early
pesticides were compounds of arsenic, copper, lead, or
zinc, or natural organic compounds such as nicotine sulphate, or some other highly toxic substance. Frequently
they killed livestock and even human beings because of
careless application.

Then came new organic pesticides, synthetically produced, with immense potency. Most were based on the
carbon molecule. The first were the chlorinated hydrocarbons, of which DDT is the best-known representative.
These resulted from the growing knowledge of organic
chemistry. Simple marsh gas, or methane, is produced
naturally when organic material decays in water. Its
formula is beautifully simple:

$$\begin{array}{ccc} H & & H \\ \diagdown & & \diagup \\ & C & \\ \diagup & & \diagdown \\ H & & H \end{array}$$

A carbon atom is surrounded by four hydrogen atoms, attached with a mechanism not thoroughly understood. Man soon learned to cut away these hydrogen atoms and replace them with chlorine, thus yielding H   Cl or

$$\begin{array}{ccc} H & & Cl \\ & \diagdown \diagup & \\ & C & \\ & \diagup \diagdown & \\ Cl & & Cl \end{array}$$

chloroform; then Cl   Cl or carbon tetrachloride.

$$\begin{array}{ccc} Cl & & Cl \\ & \diagdown \diagup & \\ & C & \\ & \diagup \diagdown & \\ Cl & & Cl \end{array}$$

Gradually chemists learned to form larger molecules consisting of rings and chains of carbon, of hydrogen, and of chlorine atoms. As early as 1874 dichloro-diphenyl-trichloro-ethane, now generally known as DDT, was synthesized. But the complex poisoning qualities of this compound were not discovered until 1939, when Swiss chemist Paul Hermann Müller initiated tests on his country's potato crop. By eliminating the Colorado potato beetle, DDT was effective in saving the crop. Widely used during World War II to kill lice on the bodies of soldiers and others, DDT was hailed as a major break-through. The men seemed to suffer no ill effects themselves, and the compound was inexpensive, easy to manufacture and to apply, and effective in killing insects and larvae. Used in immense quantities, it was spectacularly successful in virtually wiping out the malarial mosquito in countries such as India. Indeed, an estimated 85 million

Indians suffered from malaria in 1948; by 1965 the figure had fallen to 100,000. DDT was useful in exterminating many other pests that had been instrumental in killing millions of human beings.

Soon other chlorinated hydrocarbons were developed, even more effective than DDT. These overcame DDT immunities that various insects had developed. Studies of the effects of these compounds on humans were made, and gradually it became clear that large concentrations— hundreds of parts per million by weight—were toxic. It also became evident that repeated applications of these persistent compounds increased their concentrations in soil and in the bodies of fish and animals well above the level of toxicity. As these concentrations and those of newer and even more potent chlorinated hydrocarbons such as dieldrin, aldrin, and endrin grew in the 1960's, fish, animals, and birds began to suffer spectacular massacres. These disasters increased in number and in seriousness as the second group of synthetic pesticides was developed: Alkyl, or organic phosphates such as parathion and malathion were substances so toxic that they were immediately taken over by the military. It was believed that research was being done to refine them into various kinds of toxic nerve gases capable of immobilizing or killing large numbers of animals or humans, even used in minute quantities.

According to a recent U.S. Department of Agriculture report, 27 per cent of all U.S. crop acreage was being treated with herbicides or weed-killers and 12 per cent with insecticides. Here are some examples of the effects of these chemicals when used carelessly:

As early as 1944, DDT was used on an island off the coast of New Jersey to destroy flies so numerous that they were interfering with military experiments. Within a few hours the flies were dead. A week later the beaches were littered with thousands of decaying fish—which attracted even more flies from the mainland.

In the late 1940's DDT was used in a Bolivian town to destroy malarial mosquitos. It also killed all the local cats. Without the cats, the town was soon infested with rodents carrying black typhus. Before new cats could be found, several hundred people died of the disease.

In the early 1960's DDT was sprayed on Lake Sebago, the second-largest lake in Maine, to exterminate the spruce budworm, which was destroying large tracts of the state's best forests. Soon the lake shore was strewn with dead salmon. A protest and an investigation followed, during which the state forest commissioner defended the spray, claiming that DDT achieved a 98 per cent budworm kill, while causing only a 2 per cent fish kill. The investigation continues.

Wisconsin has recently been torn by argument over the same issue. During prolonged hearings, officials of the public health service asserted that the average inhabitant of the U.S. now has 12 parts of DDT per million and 0.15 parts of dieldrin in his fatty tissues, and that continued widespread use of these pesticides will cause fatalities not only of fish and birds but also of human beings.

A recent report by Michigan State University researchers asserted that DDT had caused the death of about one
million coho salmon fry in Michigan and Wisconsin
hatcheries.

In September 1967, in Tijuana, Mexico, 17 slum residents, mostly children, suddenly died in convulsions. In-
vestigators blamed local bread—the flour of which had
been made from wheat sprayed with the pesticide parathion.

As the investigations continue, DDT and other synthetic pesticides have been discovered in Arctic ice, in the
bodies of deep-sea fish, and in large quantities in soils
repeatedly sprayed or dusted. "The stuff is almost in-
destructible," remarked one expert. "It doesn't dissolve
or evaporate or deteriorate. It just goes on building
up. . . ."

Thoroughly aroused, the United Nations General Assembly passed a resolution in December 1968, to call a
world conference in 1972 on problems of pesticides and
pollution.

One of the persons responsible for focusing public
attention on this issue was the late U.S. author Rachel
Carson, whose book *Silent Spring* sold millions of copies
in many countries. Originally a marine biologist, Mrs.
Carson wrote persuasively, urging immediate measures to
prevent the pollution and poisoning of the earth. She asserted that the situation was the result not only of carelessness, but also of greedy shortsightedness on the part of the

chemical companies making pesticides. But even she did not advocate prohibiting the use of these chemicals. And experts at the FAO in Rome and elsewhere, though aware of the dangers of the misuse of pesticides, point to the immense importance of the accomplishments of the past two decades. The less-developed countries in particular have immediate need of more pesticides, say the FAO officials. Grain storage losses in India now run 25 to 50 per cent, mostly because of rats. The locust, an immensely destructive insect, does major damage in East Africa. A locust can fly 1,500 miles nonstop, thus outrunning his natural enemies. These insects reproduce three times a year, and each time the female has about 500 offspring. Every locust eats its own weight every day, and the only way known thus far to deal with them is with pesticides massively applied.

Pesticides *are* being massively applied, despite arguments and polemics. World production grew from 124 million pounds in 1947 to 637 million pounds in 1960. Millions of pounds of herbicides such as 2,4-D also are being manufactured and used for everything from killing poison ivy and ragweed to defoliating rubber plantations in Vietnam. There is every indication that their use will continue to grow.

Hopefully, in the long run, the use of poisons will begin to yield to far more refined and potentially more effective methods of combatting pests. One way is to import or breed the pests' natural enemies, or develop new breeds of parasites or antipests. Subtle ways of preventing pests from reproducing, such as sterilizing males, isolating females at breeding time, or simulating mating calls and odors, thus bewildering and frustrating males, are all possible. These pest control methods require ingenuity and initiative based on considerable knowledge of the pest's life cycle and behavior patterns, and it will be many years before they can be made to work effectively to replace poisons. Here are two examples of attempts in this direction that already have been effective:

In the late eighteenth century an enterprising Australian settler brought some prickly pears to his new home, intending to use the cactus for the manufacture of dye. Some of the plants escaped from his garden, and having no natural enemies in their new home, multiplied enormously. By 1920, some 60 million acres of good grazing land had been completely overrun. Australian entomologists investigated the prickly pear in its native habitat and found an Argentine caterpillar that fed upon it. Several billion moth eggs were taken to Australia and released. Delighted to find such large quantities of their favorite food, the caterpillars went to work and multiplied prodigiously. Within seven years the last thickets of prickly pears had been consumed and the land redeemed for grazing, at a total cost of less than one U.S. cent per acre.

The Japanese beetle was first noticed in the U.S. in 1916 in New Jersey, probably having been imported by accident. Unrestrained by natural enemies, the bugs increased rapidly, spreading throughout the eastern states and into the Midwest. In the eastern states entomologists did research and discovered some three dozen organisms that kept the beetles under control in the Orient. The most effective was a wasp called *Tiphia vernalis,* which, upon finding Japanese beetle grubs in the soil, injects a lethal dose of poison, then lays an egg on the body of the grub. When the egg hatches, the larvae eat the paralyzed grub until they are able to fend for themselves. These wasps were introduced in the eastern states and prospered. Another effective enemy of the Japanese beetle is a highly specialized kind of disease bacteria that lives in the blood of the grub. Causing the grub to turn white it has earned the name "milky disease." This organism attacks no other worms or grubs and is harmless to birds and warm-blooded animals. Both the *Tiphia* and the milky disease have been instrumental in destroying Japanese beetles in most of the eastern states. In Michigan and Illinois, however, local authorities attacked the Japanese beetle with massive DDT spray campaigns, against which thousands of residents protested, complaining that birds, cats, dogs, and even cows were the principal sufferers.

Such new systems of control are indeed desirable, but for the immediate future, poisons of various kinds will continue to play the major role. Experts of the FAO estimate that in the years immediately ahead pesticide consumption will increase at about the same rate as fertilizer consumption. To double food production in Asia, Africa, and Latin America in the next 20 years, it is estimated that 720,000 tons of pesticides will be required—six times as much as is currently being used per year. The total cost of these chemicals will be some $3.5 billion, and the effort will have to be accompanied by a widespread campaign to teach farmers to use pesticides safely.

Purposeful and massive destruction of life disturbs many sensitive or deeply religious men and women. Dr. Albert Schweitzer, for instance, in his forest hospital in Gabon would not so much as disturb a train of fire ants that were crawling up the leg of his table and systematically removing part of his supper. My father, Scott Nearing, is another example. A vegetarian, he tries to avoid killing any form of life. However, he realizes that if cutworms chew up his lettuce plants before the heads mature, he will be without lettuce. He therefore compromises: He catches the offending cutworms, puts them in a small box, and then allows volunteering guests to destroy them while he does other work. This appears to be a step ahead of humanist Leo Tolstoy, who supposedly also collected cutworms in his garden and, unwilling to allow anyone to destroy them, threw them into his neighbor's garden.

Is this discussion empty sophistry? Most pests have the ability to reproduce as fast as their food supply permits. When the act of feeding pests begins to mean starving human beings, the pests must be eliminated. They must be killed in the most efficient possible way, without harming other creatures or plants of use to man. That this attitude is immoral, presumptuous, and selfish is as obvious as it is unavoidable.

Combatting Pests

53. *One of the villains: locust specimen feeds on the scanty vegetation at Wadi in Debirene, Algeria.*

54. *Desert locusts swarm over Morocco.*

55. *Spraying California beans near Santa Clara.*

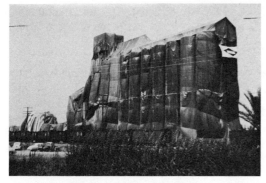

56. *Khapra beetle eradication. Grain elevator and warehouse are wrapped in gastight, plasticized tarpaulin, in preparation for fumigation with methyl bromide.*

57. *Spraying banana trees to control Sigatoka disease in Ecuador.*

58. *The Ecuadorian Institute for Agrarian Reform and Colonization provides equipment to spray fields.*

59. *Biplane dusts catalpa groves against catalpa sphinx.*

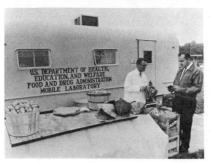

60. *Mobile laboratory of the U.S. Food and Drug Administration checks compliance with pesticide tolerances.*

7 Expanding the Meat Supply

EARLY MAN OBTAINED most of his protein and other nutrients from the animals, birds, and fish that he caught. Game animals are still an important factor in feeding Africa's hundred million people. Hippopotamus, elephant, deer, gazelle, and rabbit are staples of diet there, and in the uplands of Asia and parts of Europe, wild boar, deer, and assorted birds are systematically hunted and eaten. Small, specialized groups such as the Eskimos live almost entirely on the meat and fish they catch.

Many animals thrive on the approximate 33 per cent of the earth's land surface that is too arid or too poor to serve as cropland or efficient grazing land for domesticated animals. The management of wild animals as a potentially rich although currently poorly exploited source of animal protein is under intensive study. One group thus engaged is the FAO Wildlife Division, which has headquarters in Rome and some 70 field representatives, especially in Asia, Africa, and Latin America. It has become clear that management of immense herds of such animals as the wildebeeste—and their protection from predators and other calamities—vastly increases their potential as human food. We have also learned that intelligent cropping— sometimes as high as 25 per cent a year—can maintain stable herds of healthier animals.

The experts also have studied areas of immense waste. For example, approximately a million kangaroos were exterminated annually as pests by angry Australian farmers and buried or left to rot, although their meat is an excellent source of animal protein. There is no question that in the sparsely populated areas of the world the consumption of wild animals is likely to increase in the next generation.

In developed countries, however, and in thickly populated areas of many LDC's—India, Java, Mainland China —wild animals do not constitute an important factor in human food. Men still go hunting, of course, for deer, or duck, or quail in the U.S., for deer or boar in Europe, for rabbit, pheasant, and partridge everywhere. But it is largely sport. Take duck hunters, who are usually passionate about their sport. Scrupulous care and planning go into their trips—expensive shotguns, equipment, day-long travel to favored areas in Canada. But they admit that when the costs are totaled up, including guide, local fee, and boat rental, their duck meat costs $10 to $15 a pound.

As a source of animal protein for the majority of the

world's people, the domesticated animal has long since replaced game. Man's first domesticated animal probably was the dog—as a companion and assistant in hunting, rather than a source of food. Then came the pig, the cow, the sheep, and the goat—all bred and cared for essentially for their milk, meat, and skins. Several other multipurpose animals were of major importance to man as work animals as well as suppliers of milk, meat, and leather—the horse, the water buffalo, the camel, the llama, the yak. And, of course, since prehistoric times, chickens, ducks, geese, and turkeys have been prized for eggs, meat, and down or feathers. The numbers of domestic animals have increased more rapidly than have those of humans. The FAO estimates that currently man keeps and uses some three billion head of livestock and about the same number of domestic fowl. Considerable effort goes into their breeding and feeding and into the elimination of the parasites and diseases that afflict them.

During recent generations, man's patient efforts have been aided by his increasing knowledge of genetics, making possible major improvements in the efficiency of domestic animals. The best merino sheep in Australia produce many times more wool than did their ancestors who first lived in Spain many centuries ago. A good holstein cow gives several times as much milk per year as did her progenitor in medieval Europe. Perhaps the most intensive and rewarding genetic efforts have been made on the chicken. The late Henry A. Wallace, although better known as a politician, was a geneticist of stature, first famous for his work in developing hybrid corn. Toward the end of his life, however, he worked with chickens. Visitors to his farm in South Salem, New York, were always impressed by the care with which some 5,000 chickens were meticulously studied as to food intake, gain in weight, and the size, frequency, color, and nutrient content of eggs. Mutations were stimulated by inbreeding and other ways of producing abnormalities in structure and growth patterns. By careful cross-breeding the desirable characteristics—large eggs for laying hens, quick growth and high meat content for broilers—were retained and undesirable characteristics bred out. The result was chickens that yielded animal protein at an efficiency coefficient of roughly 25 per cent. This means that the food consumed by the bird is reflected by one-fourth as much meat food value. Other domesticated creatures are not so efficient: The hog is probably next with an efficiency of about 20 per cent, cow's milk reflects perhaps 18 per cent of the food its production required, and a good cut of beef contains only about one-seventh the food value the steer consumed before it became beefsteak. This is the basic reason that most people in the LDC's eat principally grain, vegetables, and fruit, and regard meat and dairy products as luxuries for special occasions.

According to nutritionist Aaron Altschul, the cost factor is the main reason for the wide disparity in the distribution of animal protein. For example, U.S. citizens have available 1,650 pounds of grain per person per year, but consume only 150 pounds. The remaining 1,500 pounds is fed to animals, which are then eaten. The Eastern Indians have available only 340 pounds of grain per person per year; it has been estimated that they eat 295 pounds of it, leaving almost none for feeding animals. Thus, an animal protein economy exists only when there is a surplus of grain over human requirements to be fed to animals.

Almost all human beings would like to improve the quality and variety of their diet; many would like to eat more animal protein. One indication of this is the structure of the diet of people in the world's most affluent countries, such as the U.S.; they eat far more animal than vegetable protein, a situation that is not desirable. Most people in the U.S. and western Europe consume more saturated fats than is good for their circulatory systems, and this is one cause of cardiac ailments that directly result in many deaths.

For most of the human race, however, this is not a problem. They suffer from protein deficiency, they want more meat and dairy products, and they would be healthier and longer-lived if they got them. For these millions, more efficient cropping of game and improved breeds of hogs, cattle, and fowl will be instrumental in rectifying their current protein deficiency.

Yet, in many areas where malnutrition is most prevalent, animal husbandry is most retarded. A striking and well-publicized example is India's sacred cow. India has about 175 million cows—about one-third of the world's bovine population. Nearly half of these have no fixed domicile nor owner. Respected and protected as holy animals, they wander about—skinny, diseased, blocking traffic in the cities, eating whatever crops they can find in rural areas. They are too poorly nourished to furnish an appreciable amount of milk, and no attempt is made to improve the stock by selective breeding, since one does not coerce a sacred animal. When they grow old and infirm, a few are consigned to community homes for old cows called gosadans, but most die uncared for. Any attempt to fatten the cows for use as food is violently opposed by members of the anti-cow-slaughter party.

Irrational? Perhaps. But is it any more rational for people in the U.S. to breed cows that grow very fat within a relatively short period with the result that much of the population dies of heart attacks from overeating in general and overconsumption of saturated fats in particular?

8 From Neptune's Kingdom

ALTHOUGH FISH COMES last in a discussion of food production, fishing is neither new nor unimportant for feeding human beings. Indeed, it is one of the oldest sources of food, and the 1967 world catch of 60 million tons meant a yearly average of 38 pounds of fish per person. Since 1945, world fish production has increased at a fairly steady rate of 5 to 6 per cent a year, or more than twice as rapidly as the human race has been multiplying. Most fish, however, come from the high seas, which are under the jurisdiction of no one nation. It is a world resource, therefore, and must receive different consideration. It is, one might say, everyone's property, a shared responsibility.

Man probably first caught freshwater fish, and despite massive pollution of our lakes and rivers, people still get some food from this source. In several countries fish farming has long been practiced. In China, for example, artificial ponds were stocked with fingerlings, which were fed with silkworms that had completed their delicate job. Silk was the farmer's cash crop, rice his staple, and fish the source of his protein. In Germany and Austria, trout farms made up of a series of ponds have produced excellent fish for years in far greater quantities than could have been caught in local streams. More sophisticated projects are now under way, such as the fish farm complex in landlocked Nepal, which will produce several hundreds of thousands of pounds of fish to supplement the protein-poor diet of the rugged Sherpa people.

Of course, the sea produces far more fish, and its potential is infinitely greater than that of fresh water. Let us look at the 1967 catch.

The world seafood harvest has been growing steadily since just after World War II, and this healthy trend continued in 1967. The world catch was about 60 million tons, up by approximately 5 per cent over 1966. The Centrally Planned Economies, as FAO calls the Communist countries, made substantial gains, as did many LDC's. The world's five leading fishing countries—Peru, Japan, Mainland China, the U.S.S.R., and Norway, along with South and Southwest Africa, were the principal gainers.

Peru's catch of ten million tons led to the production of 1.8 million tons of fish meal, 23 per cent more than in the previous year. Japan was second with 7.7 million tons, most of which was utilized for direct human consumption. The more than three million tons caught by the Norwegians in 1967 was double that of 1964, and on several occasions the Norwegian fishermen outran the reduction capacity of their fish-meal factories and had to suspend operation temporarily. High production forced prices down, so that the value of the 1967 catch was actually less than that of the smaller 1966 tonnage.

World prices do not affect Mainland China or the Soviet Union, both of which reported excellent catches, which they consumed domestically. The U.S.S.R. fulfilled its plan of 5.7 million tons—about 8 per cent more than in 1966. China has released no figures. Increasingly, the U.S.S.R. is operating fleets of trawlers and other fishing boats attached to huge factory vessels, which for months operate virtually independently, thousands of miles from their home ports. In Sydney, Australia, for example, in early 1968 a Soviet whaling fleet came to port. The fleet had been at sea for nine months and had caught 3,321 whales. To the astonishment of Soviet critics, the commander of the fleet released $250,000 in Australian currency to the 1,200 men and women on the 21 vessels to spend in Sydney.

Not so vigorous in their fishing efforts were the U.S., Chile, Canada, Iceland, and the United Kingdom. The U.S. catch was the lowest in 25 years. Only in shrimp and tuna did the U.S. fishermen have a good year in 1967. The Canadians were hampered by a poor salmon run in the North Pacific, and the Chileans by an unexplained shortage of anchovettas off their long Pacific coast. Reduced availability of herring was principally responsible for the

Icelanders' subnormal catch, although low prices for both fillets and meal were additional factors. India and other Far Eastern shrimp-fishing nations had a fine year, as did the fishermen off the coasts of South and Southwest Africa, famous for shrimp and lobster. Middle East fishermen had a fair year, but in North Africa the Algerians increased their catch by 25 per cent, the Tunisians by slightly less.

All the world's nations try to assert their sovereignty over the sea adjacent to their shores. Most claim either a three-mile limit—probably based on the range of an ancient cannon—or a twelve-mile limit as the demarcation of their territorial waters. But some countries have shores that constitute outcroppings of a broad continental shelf; these nations have sometimes asserted claims of more than 200 miles of the adjacent sea. Most nations have twelve-mile limits for fishing rights, however. Major disputes have arisen, a famous one being Brazil's attempts to keep French lobster fishermen away from Brazilian shores, resulting in a confrontation between the two countries in the mid-1960's. To avoid such disputes, many agreements have been concluded between nations that fish close to each other's shores. Such agreements among the Soviet Union, the two Koreas, and Japan regulate fishing areas and catches in the Sea of Japan and the Sea of Okhotsk. Similar agreements between Britain and Iceland seek to regulate the fishing of herring in the waters in that part of the world.

Although in a biological sense whales are not fish,

but mammals, their capture is considered part of the fishing industry. It is the only part of the fishing industry that has been subjected to fairly comprehensive multilateral regulation. The agreements concluded among the principal whaling nations—Japan, the U.S.S.R., Norway, the U.S., and the U.K.—sought to restrict catches to a level compatible with the maintenance of the most valuable species, particularly the blue whale and the sperm whale. During the years since World War II, however, the size and efficiency of the whaling fleets have increased, and catches have declined. Since 1968, when Norway discontinued whaling operations, the field has been left largely to Japan and the Soviet Union. Their efforts, however, are so vigorous and so competitive that there is some danger that the whale may become extinct.

There is also substantial danger that other species of sea life may be "fished out," particularly those that spawn in freshwater streams, which in parts of the world have become polluted. In this category are the salmon and the tuna—two of the most popular fish. The Fisheries Department of the FAO is working hard today to prevent this through regulation, but progress has been slow.

By far the most numerous fish are those of the herring-anchovy family. For example, the Peruvian fish-meal catch is almost entirely anchovettas, which are about six inches long and thrive in immense quantities off the western coasts of Latin America, sometimes shifting north and south with changes in the Humboldt Current. Sturdy fishing boats from Lima go some 20 miles from shore and in minutes scoop their holds full of fish, along with an occasional angry sea lion. In port, the anchovettas are sucked through 12-inch pipes from the vessels into the boilers of the fish-meal plants. The meal, worth about $100 a ton, is used mostly for animal fodder. High in protein content, it can be made into fish protein concentrate (FPC), a wonderfully nutritious substance that is colorless, odorless, tasteless, and stable, and therefore ideally suited to fortify grain or other foods poor in protein. This has been inhibited in the U.S., however, by the longstanding position of the Food and Drug Administration (FDA) that any product made from a whole fish is unfit for human consumption. Although the FDA has now changed its ruling, so far only pilot plants are making FPC. The chapter on nutrition discusses this further.

Oceanography is still a young science, and man is just beginning to study the sea's flora and fauna with discipline comparable to other sciences. Thanks to the observations of divers, bathyscopes, and other study methods, oceanographers estimate that the sea produces about 130 billion tons of vegetable matter yearly. Much of this consists of microscopic algae-like cells, which are eaten by tiny organisms known collectively as plankton. The plankton is in turn eaten by small fish, and they by larger fish. The annual growth of fish in the sea is perhaps three billion tons, of which about 300 million tons inhabit the 10 per cent or so of the ocean lying on continental shelves, where fish can be caught with present techniques. Most experts believe that the present catch could be increased safely by fourfold, taking 40 per cent of the annual growth without jeopardizing Poseidon's kingdom. Care would have to be taken not to fish out the most popular species, however. Further in the future, improved techniques should make it possible to tap the deeper seas where some 90 per cent of the fish live. The fishing industry has benefited from electronic research undertaken during recent years by several nations for military purposes. One of the most striking examples was the discovery in the 1950's of a previously unknown layer of herring in the 200- to 400-foot depth area. The Norwegians and Icelanders proceeded forthwith to innovate equipment to catch the fish.

The world's shellfish catch is not yet nearly as large a percentage of the annual growth as the fish catch, and one may anticipate—with new efficient techniques of catching and freezing—that shrimp, crawfish, crab, and lobster will continue to grow as excellent sources of protein for human beings.

Sea farming is still in its prehistory period. The Japanese eat a bit of seaweed, but as a delicacy. No attempt has been made to breed varieties of seaweed on the continental shelves, where water is shallow enough to allow the sun's rays to penetrate and permit photosynthesis to take place. There the nutrients for plant growth, which we examined in the analysis of soil, are available from the sand and mud of the ocean floor and from the sea itself. That the roots, berries, beans, or seeds of such seaweed could be used for human food is another example of the vast and untapped potential of the sea.

Many Ways to Net a Catch

61. "Fishing" with a can opener.

62. Factory in Agadir, Morocco, produces fishmeal for both animal and human consumption—part of the World Food Program.

63. Plankton, sole food of the anchoveta, is studied by the Peruvian Sea Institute.

64. *Japanese fishermen repair nets at Enashima.*

65. *Stone weights are part of this Peruvian fisherman's net.*

66. *Fishing in an Egyptian water ditch.*

67. *Turkish fishermen cast nets in the Aegean Sea near Kusadasi.*

68. *Hauling codfish aboard near the New Brunswick coast.*

69. *Injecting pituitary gland extract into female carp increases breeding at Hlawga Fisheries Station near Rangoon, Burma.*

70. *Fertilized eggs are placed in hatching hapas, which consist of an inner mosquito net and an outer close-meshed net.*

71. *Salmon being hoisted to canneries at Juneau, Alaska.*

72. *Chinese fisherman spikes salted fish on pole for drying.*

73. *Fish for sale from the Congo River, at Kinkole, in the Congo.*

74. *Japanese store typically displays many types of fish.*

75. *Drying fish in Hokkaido, Japan, to make fertilizer.*

9 The ABC's of Nutrition

MOST PEOPLE THINK of feeding the hungry in quantitative terms—growing more food for more people. It is important, however, to consider the qualitative element as well —the nutritional quality of foods—and how this might be improved.

Nutrition is the process by which an animal or plant takes in and utilizes food substances. Metabolism is the process that transforms food into energy and living tissue. Two related chemical processes make up metabolism— catabolism, the breaking down of food substances to release energy, and anabolism, the synthesis or building up of new cells and tissues and repair of worn-out tissues. These functions are carried out during the process of digestion.

Let us examine what happens during the digestive process. Food, consisting of three main kinds of organic compounds—proteins, fats, and carbohydrates—enters the body and is broken down in the digestive tract. Chewing is the first step, for in the mouth the small food particles meet the starch-splitting enzyme of the saliva. The muscular walls of the stomach churn the food, break it into smaller particles, and secrete pepsin, as well as hydrochloric acid. When the food is passed into the small intestine, it meets bile from the gall bladder and enzyme-rich juices from the pancreas. The bile breaks fat into finer globules. Carbohydrates, proteins, and fats are further broken down by the pancreatic juices. The end products of digestion are simple sugars, formed by the breakdown of carbohydrates and fatty acids; glycerol, by the breakdown of fats; and amino acids, from the protein breakdown. The latter are recombined in predetermined proportions to rebuild the various proteins of the body. For optimum tissue building, it is essential that the component amino acids be present in definite proportions; the rate of the process becomes limited by the amount of the amino acid least available.

The end products of digestion are absorbed by the body, largely in the small intestine, because few foods are broken into absorbable units before they reach that part of the alimentary tract. The absorptive surface of the small intestine is increased by its great length—ten feet in adult man—and by the several folds and projections in its internal surface. The large intestine removes water from

the residues of digestion and forms feces, which are ex-
creted from the body.

The small units or "food fuels" absorbed primarily by
the small intestine are carried by the blood stream to all
tissues of the body. They may be used by the cells as
building blocks for new growing tissue or be burned to
produce energy and/or heat.

Human nutrition begins at the moment that an egg cell
is fertilized by a sperm. The nutrition given to the first
subdividing cells exerts a profound influence that may be
felt throughout life. All cells of the body—from bone
cells to hair-building cells and heart cells—must be nourished satisfactorily in order to remain alive and well.

Nutritional needs in the first ten years of life are relatively higher than in any later period. It is unfortunate
that the meeting of these needs is almost completely dependent upon other people, usually the mother and father.
Often, they themselves are poorly fed or do not understand the special needs of the young child.

In addition to the functions already mentioned, the key
nutrients perform other vital works for the body. Protein
helps build blood and form antibodies to fight infection.
This function, combined with its tissue-building and
energy-supplying role, makes it a vital food substance.
Whereas an adult needs about 0.7 gram of protein daily
per kilo of body weight, a child in the first three months
of life needs three to four times as much. Protein from
animal sources is of a higher quality than that from plant

sources, and for this reason, less of the former is needed for adequate nutrition. As we have noted, in the developed countries most protein comes from animal sources—meat, milk, eggs, fish. About 39 grams of animal protein per capita per day is consumed. The rest of the world, however, gets protein from the cereals—wheat, rice, and corn—and consumes only seven grams of animal protein per capita daily. The worldwide range in per capita animal protein consumption is from two to 52 pounds yearly.

Fat supplies large amounts of energy in a small amount of food. Although overconsumption, especially of saturated fats, has received much attention in industrialized countries as a cause of heart disease, far less interest has been shown in the risks of inadequate consumption of fat. Its sources are butter and cream, fat in meat, and salad oils and dressings. Carbohydrates—sugars and starches—are primarily energy suppliers and are more or less adjusted to filling out what is consumed in the form of protein and fats. They are found in sugar, honey, bread, cereal, potatoes, corn and beans, and fruit. Sugar and pure starches provide calories only, but starchy roots and cereals contain some protein, vitamins, and minerals as well. Of course, vitamins and minerals are necessary for a balanced diet.

Although minerals are needed by adults in only small quantities, children need relatively large amounts of them. Minerals function in the body as constituents of bones and in the strengthening of structural parts of soft tissues. Calcium in particular builds bones and teeth, aids in blood clotting and the functioning of muscles and nerves, and helps regulate the use of other minerals in the body. It is found principally in milk, cheese, ice cream, and some vegetable greens. A child's daily requirement of calcium is estimated at .7 to .8 gram. Iron combines with protein in the body to make hemoglobin, the red substance in the blood that carries oxygen to the cells; a child needs about 10 mg. per day. Liver, other meat, eggs, and some leafy vegetables and grain cereals are its main suppliers. Iodine helps control the rate at which the body uses energy; it is found in seafood, in plants grown in soil near seas, and in iodized salt. Phosphorus must be taken in the ratio of 1:1 with calcium to permit normal bone development; it also helps nerve tissue formation and muscle contraction. Eggs, fish, milk, and cereals are principal sources.

Other minerals needed are sodium and potassium chlorides—important for improved appetite and prevention of muscular weakness and mental apathy—and cobalt, zinc, copper, nitrogen, sulfur, fluorine, and more than 30 others.

Vitamins are organic substances, essential in minute quantities to the nutrition of most animals and some plants. They help regulate metabolic processes, although they do not provide energy or serve as building units. Principal vitamins include vitamin A, which is needed for normal vision, healthy skin, and body, and is found in liver, shellfish, and some fresh vegetables and fruits. Several important vitamins are in the B complex group: Thiamine (vitamin B_1), which promotes appetite and preserves the nervous system, is found in vegetables, lean meat, and whole grain cereals; and vitamin B₂ (ribo-flavin), which serves to prevent hair loss, skin changes, paralysis, and sore eyes and tongue, is found principally in whole grains, meats, vegetable leaves, milk, and liver. Niacin, which protects against skin and digestive troubles and preserves the nerves, is found in meats, fish, nuts, milk, and cooked cereals. Vitamin C, or ascorbic acid, aids nutrient utilization and protects teeth and gums. Its sources are green vegetables, fruits, and fresh roots. Vitamin D, also known as the sunshine vitamin, serves to prevent rickets and promotes fixation of bone minerals. Cod-liver oil, liver, and milk are rich in this vitamin. Vitamin E, necessary for fertility and virility, is present in cereals, oils, meat, green leaves, and eggs. Vitamin K, necessary for blood clotting, is found primarily in spinach, cabbage, and pork.

Measuring Consumption

When food is consumed, the amount of energy that it produces is expressed in terms of calories. Specifically, one calorie is the amount of heat required to raise the temperature of one gram of water by one degree centigrade at a pressure of one atmosphere. Obviously, it is important to eat foods that provide large amounts of the nutrients discussed above in addition to calories to provide energy.

With this background, consider the world nutrition picture at the present time. One billion people in the developed countries consume half again as many calories and five times as much high-quality animal protein per person as the two billion people in the less-developed countries, reports the National Advisory Commission on Food and Fiber. Thus:

	Developed Countries	LDC'S
Average daily caloric consumption per person	2,941	2,033
Average total protein consumption per person, daily grams	84.0	52.4
Average animal protein consumption only, per person, daily grams	38.8	7.2

The genetic differences that create a lesser average body weight in many LDC's slightly mitigate the disadvantage shown by the table. Physical activity is another influencing variable. However, even taking these factors into account, the differences are marked. The Third World Food Survey conducted by the FAO in 1963 indicated that 60 per cent of the population of the LDC's received diets of inadequate nutritional quality and at least 20 per cent were undernourished. Reports published since 1952 suggest that nearly 10 per cent of preschool children of developing countries have kwashiorkor (protein malnutrition) and marasmus (calorie malnutrition). Other nutritional disorders found to be prevalent were hypovitaminosis A, the lack of adequate vitamin A that leads to night blindness and sometimes permanent total blindness; thiamine deficiency or beriberi, occurring mostly in countries in which rice is the staple food; hyporiboflavinosis, riboflavin deficiency that causes buccal mucosa; and pellagra, caused by deficiency of niacin and associated mainly with diets based on maize. Goiter, a grossly enlarged thyroid gland resulting from inadequate iodine, and rickets, soft or deformed bones caused by lack of vitamin D, are also fairly common in the LDC's.

Particularly ironic has been the graphic evidence of serious malnutrition in the United States, as reported by the U.S. Senate Committee on Nutrition and Human Needs. On January 22, 1968, Dr. Arnold E. Schaefer of the U.S. Public Health Service reported that of 12,000 people examined (mostly from Texas, Louisiana, and Kentucky, with several hundred more people from upper New York State), 17 per cent were undernourished enough to be considered genuine "medical risks." Statistics indicated, furthermore, that one of every three children under six years of age in the study was anemic and 3.5 per cent were physically stunted, a condition often accompanied by mental retardation.

A resurgence of several of the diseases mentioned above was also reported—diseases believed to have been eradicated in the 1930's: Five per cent of those studied had goiter. Although iodized salt capable of preventing this disorder costs no more than regular salt, many stores do not stock it. By adding vitamin D to milk in the 1930's, rickets was virtually eliminated from the U.S.; today not all milk sold in U.S. stores has vitamin D added, although such fortified milk is required for U.S. food programs overseas, and rickets is returning in the U.S. Seven cases of kwashiorkor were found among those examined in the study, and nearly a third of the children six or under suffered from night blindness.

Thus, malnutrition poses an agonizing threat to both the developed and less-developed worlds—to the human race itself. A poorly nourished population cannot perform effectively and perpetuates its own poverty.

What Can Be Done?

Many nutritionists such as Aaron Altschul feel that conventional approaches alone will not suffice: Poor populations are growing poorer and larger. These experts believe that solutions to the problem lie in several major areas: (1) total upgrading of national food supply by improving quality of major cereals; (2) more efficient use of food from the sea; and (3) developing new foods, either by fortifying existing foods or creating new protein foods. The first category involves adding a higher protein quality to cereals by fortification with amino acids, vitamins, and minerals. The three essential amino acids in which most cereal grains are deficient are lysine, threonine, and trytophan. Mass-production factory methods could produce lysine for as little as $1 per pound. The others can be synthesized for about $2.50 to $4.50 per pound, but mass production could probably reduce the price to that of lysine. Varied combinations of patterns of nitrogen, hydrogen, and carbon—synthetic materials—can be produced as colorless, odorless, tasteless crystals. They can be introduced into an existing food at a central processing point—a flour or corn meal mill—and consumers would in no way have to change their food consumption habits. In 1967, the U.S. Department of Agriculture had projected that by 1969 all emergency grain shipments from the U.S. would be fortified with protein concentrates or amino acids, but recent budget cuts have slowed this program. One drawback in fortifying cereal grain is that people who may not need the improved protein quality will also get the fortified material, unnecessarily increasing the cost of such a program. Greater efficiency can be achieved and the fortification process eliminated by increasing the natural protein content of the world's principal cereal crops through "genetic manipulation." This has been done most successfully with corn; the opaque-2 variety contains about 65 per cent more lysine, more trytophan, and a better amino acid balance than ordinary hybrid corn. New varieties of wheat, rice, sorghum, and millet with higher protein content and greater yield have been discussed in an earlier chapter. Although this approach to the nutrition problem holds great promise, considerable time is needed to develop sufficient seed and to persuade farmers throughout the world to use it.

Out of 25,000 known species of fish, only a few dozen are utilized by man as food, either directly or indirectly. Even more pertinent is the fact that in protein-deficient countries—Asia, Africa, and Latin America—the consumption of fish products, both marine and freshwater, is only about seven pounds yearly per person, partly because of superstition and prejudice. Estimates show that the annual catch of saltwater fish could be greatly increased without endangering the oceanic food chain, but this tremendous potential would require time and money to tap—ships, ports, and processing and storage facilities. Fish farming in inland fisheries as a means of further increasing the catch was discussed in a previous section on fish. Indeed, the utilization of the world's fish resources could greatly improve the world's protein picture. Some species of fish are equally as efficient protein producers as chickens, and considerably more so than pigs and other domesticated animals raised for food. Fish protein concentrate—possibly the most efficient use of a greatly increased fish harvest— will be discussed shortly.

Another approach to the malnutrition problem involves new foods made by fortifying conventional products such as bread, tortilla flour, and bakery goods. Advantages of fortification are speed, economy, simplicity, and the fact that it does not require mass education. The cost of fortification usually runs 2 to 10 per cent of the cost of the grain.

Protein concentrate extracted from oil seeds—soybeans, cotton seed, and peanuts—is a prime example. Concentrate from soybeans ranges from 40 to 95 per cent protein content, and costs from 14 to 50 U.S. cents per pound. The material is quite versatile—it can be used as an additive to cereal products, flours, and high-protein beverages; and it can be processed into a wide range of products that are virtually indistinguishable from real meat. Protein pulp is spun into long bands of fibers as thin as three-thousandths of an inch, and changes in fiber size determine texture. By adding nutrients, color, and artificial flavors, almost any food can be imitated—chicken, bacon, beef, ham, and others.

Soybean flour may be processed in areas where neither skilled labor nor electrical power is available. In one working day five men can produce 300 pounds of soya flour— enough to supply the daily protein requirements for 1,600 adults. Cottonseed—after removal of oil and seed coat— yields a concentrate with 50 to 55 per cent protein, and after further concentration, with 70 per cent protein.

The Institute of Nutrition of Central America in Panama has developed several formulas from a corn base supplemented by sesame, cottonseed, or soybeans, plus yeast. Called Incaparina, the mixture resembles corn meal and can be used to prepare traditional dishes made of corn meal. A subsidiary of the Quaker Oats Company has been marketing Incaparina in Cali, Colombia, for about six years; about 30 per cent of the population in urban areas now consume the product. The cost is very low—approximately one-fifth that of milk, and it boasts the same nutritional value. Similar formulas are being introduced in other parts of the world and can be of major value in helping to meet the protein shortage.

Another concentrate comes from that much neglected protein source—fish. Fish protein concentrate (FPC), about 80 per cent protein, costs more than soybean or other vegetable concentrates per unit of protein, but this is still not prohibitive. About 25 grams of FPC provide sufficient protein per day for an adult. But some problems of consumer acceptance remain, and as we have already mentioned, bureaucratic impediments with such agencies as the U.S. Food and Drug Administration are only beginning to be overcome. It is encouraging, however, that U.S. AID teams are testing protein-rich fish flour as a food additive in Chile, Peru, Brazil, and India. In 1968, AID (Agency for International Development) issued a request for proposals to build a fish-flour plant in Latin America.

Private and Public Partnership

The oilseed beverages are important as a new food product to fight malnutrition and also because they represent partnership between private enterprise and public distribution. Vitasoy, a high-protein cola developed from soybeans by a Chinese businessman, is a good example. Cheaper in Hong Kong than Coca-Cola, it contains 5.9 grams of protein per bottle and has captured 25 per cent of the Hong Kong soft-drink market. The Monsanto Company of St. Louis has now joined forces with the creators of Vitasoy and has devised a new, more flavorful drink called Puma; first franchise operations are being set up in Guyana and Taiwan. The Coca-Cola Company plans to make a new high-protein drink in Brazil called Saci. Chocolate-flavored and soybean-based, Saci contains seven vitamins and 3 per cent protein. In El Salvador the Pillsbury Company is consumer-testing a new soft drink made from corn meal, cottonseed, and nut meal.

Today between 80 and 100 companies and organizations around the world are trying to develop commercially viable high-protein products. An experimental three-year U.S. AID program calls for about six companies to be financed yearly. In addition to Monsanto and Pillsbury, these include Swift (soybean foods for Brazil), Krause Milling (fortified corn food for Brazil), International Milling (high protein wheat foods for Tunisia), and Dorr-Oliver (cottonseed protein concentrate for India). There seems to be much commercial interest in the program.

Still another potential source of protein for the hungry is fossil protein. A number of major petroleum firms have undertaken feasibility studies of making single-cell proteins on bases of once-living compounds. These proteins are produced by the activities of microorganisms—principally yeasts and bacteria—growing on such bases as sucrose, molasses, soybean oil, kerosene, petroleum distillate No. 2, waste paper, surplus and spoiled fruits and vegetables, lumber industry waste products, and methane gas. The cost of protein produced in this manner is on the order of from 20 to 40 cents per pound, more expensive than protein contained in oilseed meal. Most experts agree that significant contributions to world nutrition from this kind of protein production lie far in the future.

Thus, there are a number of ways in which man might improve the nutrition of the human race—some more immediately available, some under intense study for the next century.

Bread—the Basis

76. *An English bake shop window.*

77. *Crushing grain for bread in the Kraal district of South Africa.*

78. *Indian children in Guiana cutting* cassava.

79. *Making* chapattis *in India.*

80. Warm cinnamon rolls, from an oven, in the U.S.

81. Chileñian corn-bread in the making.

82. Somi from Greece.

83. *A woman in Honduras makes* tortillas *on a stone* metate.

84. *Out of Egyptian ovens comes traditional flat bread of the country.*

*85. Loaves are delivered
in carts in France.*

86. Bread stalls in Moroccan market.

10 To Market, To Market

IF MOST MEN produced food for themselves and their families only our survey of seed, soil, water, fertilizer, pest control, and other factors would have constituted a reasonably complete picture of man's struggle against hunger.

But in today's complex world, most food producers in the developed countries grow their crops "for the market" —that is, for other consumers—and buy their own food in stores. Even in the LDC's, millions of city-dwellers produce no food, and sometimes entire countries live largely on imported food.

This modern specialization has made necessary a network of institutions and procedures between production and consumption of food. Crops must be harvested, transported to central granaries, stored, processed, packaged, moved to retail outlets, merchandised, and sold. Further-more, the producer and each person involved in the long train of interim operations must be motivated. He must have an incentive to work. For the primitive farmer or fisherman who produced for himself and his family, in-centive took care of itself. He got hungry, and he worked. But with the separation of production and consumption, incentives had to be created.

In antiquity most producers were slaves and worked under pain of death or torture. In more modern societies, however, most people have produced, transported, and processed food for some kind of pay or profit—a share of the price paid by the ultimate consumer. Since months or even years elapsed between the time food was produced and its consumption, some mechanism of financing was necessary to support the train of usually poor men and women involved in production until the food was finally eaten and paid for, and each participant in the process could get his share of the realized price. This role was at one time filled by the feudal lord, or the money-lender. More recently it has become the function of banks and other credit institutions. Even more recently, in the world's centrally administered economies, government has taken over the responsibility of organizing and financing these interim operations, and in some cases has even outlawed subsistence farming altogether.

Since the world today consists of societies functioning on various levels of historic evolution, perhaps we should mention several of these kinds of society.

In tribal communities such as those of the Montagnards of Vietnam, the Indians in the Andes, and tribesmen in much of Sumatra and New Guinea, men live more or less self-sufficiently on what they produce on land owned in common or by some far-off ruler. They pay a tax or tribute to the local chief who protects them from external enemies and maintains internal "order."

In feudal societies, such as those of Europe before the French Revolution, the South before the U.S. Civil War, Japan before the Meiji Restoration of 1868, and much of Latin America today, the land belonged to a few wealthy families. It was tilled by serfs or peasants, who worked hard, consumed little, and were unable to better their lot because of physical restraints, illiteracy, or constant indebtedness.

Gradually, as a result of peasant rebellions and the development of social conscience among owners and their intellectual associates, the institution of slavery was overthrown. But freedom without education or opportunity proved to be a frustrating delusion to millions—until they were able to acquire title to their land or to learn to farm it effectively. This was accomplished in "empty" lands such as the U.S. by homesteading, except that in the process Negroes were deliberately excluded from such benefits. In older and more densely populated areas, it was accomplished by land reforms such as those carried out in much of Europe after the French Revolution, in Russia after 1917, or during recent years in Iran.

Here a major difference occurred. In some countries

settlers or newly emancipated serfs retained control of
their land; in others, governments rapidly took control
of the land and forced the peasantry into a new kind of
serfdom.

Countries in the former category—Western Europe,
most of North America, Oceania, and parts of East Asia
and Latin America—became largely farmer-owner economies, in which the food producer owned his land, grew
what he wanted, sold it for the best price, and consumed
the profits as he wished. He had, of course, many problems. He was frequently exploited by the railroads, the
banks, and the suppliers of the machinery and fertilizer
he needed. He had to pay taxes. Sometimes he was forced
out of business by low-cost imported foods from areas
overseas or by greedy neighbors who took advantage of
his misfortune or misjudgment. Often prices fluctuated
wildly, leaving him rich one year, starving the next. To
protect himself from these hazards, the farmer banded
with others into cooperatives like those in Scandinavia,
or into political parties with excellent results. Together,
they often were able to force reluctant governments to
support farm product prices, to bar competitive imports,
and in other ways to protect their interests. Being reasonably sure that they would benefit directly from larger
crops, they strove to produce more. This conviction and
hard work, along with the help of government organizations and educational institutions, stimulated enormously
increased productivity.

As farms grew larger and more mechanized, the number of farmers dwindled, until today in the U.S. they comprise only about 5 per cent of the total labor force. But farmers still retain extensive political power in the U.S., Western Europe, Canada, Japan, and elsewhere. Their influence is so great indeed that the U.S. government currently spends some $5 billion a year on agricultural subsidies and assorted agricultural services such as county agents who provide information and guidance to farmers. Food production has continued to increase, and these countries have emerged in the past generation as the world's great granary nations.

The Socialist States

Eastern Europe, the Soviet Union, and China took a different road. The food producers were forced to accept a secondary status in a "dictatorship of the proletariat." These millions saw little point in working hard to increase their crops because they rapidly learned that the state took everything and returned to them little more than they needed to live. When they resisted, as the *kulaks* (well-to-do peasants) did in Russia in the early 1930's, millions were dispossessed and driven into prison camps, where they starved. Discouraged and desperate, other millions left the land and sought jobs in industry or construction, leaving their country short of food.

Stalin's reasons for collectivization seemed clear enough. He wanted to remove the possibility of peasant-based political opposition. He wanted the peasantry to work hard and consume little so that he could use the surplus for industrialization; and it may be argued that in so doing, he saved Russia from what might have been a disastrous defeat at the hands of industrialized Germany. But in agriculture the Soviet record is uninspiring.

The territory that is now the U.S.S.R. was at one time the granary of Europe. In 1913, Russia exported nine million tons of grain and was the world's largest producer and exporter. Although devastated and disorganized by a lost war, by a revolution, and by a civil war, Soviet agriculture displayed a spectacular recovery in the middle 1920's under the New Economic Policy, which successfully encouraged peasants to produce and get rich. Almost ten million *kulaks* led a burst of agricultural productivity culminating in the crop of 1927, which equaled the bumper harvest of 1913 and placed the country again in a position to afford substantial exports. But the *kulaks* also became a political threat to the Soviet government, which was bitterly opposed to private enterprise of any kind. In one of the most violent moves in the world's agricultural history, the government forced collectivization of agriculture over a period of three years. During that time farmers slaughtered about half of the country's livestock rather than allow the animals to be collectivized, several million peasants died of starvation as grain was taken to feed industrial and construction workers, and the *kulaks* were "liquidated." The rationale behind this policy was that it made possible the rapid industrialization of the country by squeezing resources from the agricultural sector.

By the middle 1930's, however, it was clear that the *kolkhozy,* or collective farms, were not working well, and that a more voluntary system of agricultural organization would probably increase production. But by that time the collective-farm system had been written into the Constitution of 1936 and had become a part of the ideology of communism. There is no evidence that Stalin ever considered decollectivization, but if he had, he would have been forced to acknowledge the needless killing of millions. Rather than subjecting the collective-farm system to critical study and fundamental revision, Stalin canonized it as the "road to Communism" and imposed it directly on millions in East Europe who fell under Soviet control after World War II.

In recent years Yugoslavia became independent enough politically to carry out its own policies and to decollectivize its agriculture. The resulting increase of food production encouraged Poland, which also contrived a substantial liquidation of the collectives in favor of "circles," or loose-knit cooperatives. The rest of the Communist world, however, clung to a system that was instrumental in the steady deterioration of the agricultural sector and meant virtual serfdom for millions of hungry peasants. Without internal passports they could not leave the collective farms, where they remained unproductive and politically dangerous. Indeed, there is a good deal of evidence to suggest that if Hitler had had the political acumen to dissolve the *kolkhozy* in the areas he captured in 1941, he would have gained a decisive advantage for his own ends. But he regarded the *kolkhozy* as useful instruments of enslavement, and retained them.

After Stalin's death, Khrushchev tinkered unsuccessfully with Soviet agriculture. He insisted on planting corn in areas too cold and dry. He had 100 million acres of "virgin lands" plowed in Kazakhstan, Siberia, and central Asia without adequate provision for anti-erosion measures—with disastrous results. He experimented with the size of the collective farms, decentralized and then recentralized their management, and organized a huge campaign to increase the production and use of manufactured fertilizer—which, unfortunately, produced more noise than nitrogen.

Concurrent with the economic reforms initiated by courageous critics such as Professor Evsei Liberman, Soviet politicians began discussing the possibility of fundamental revision of the collective-farm system. Under the old system, small private kitchen gardens were permitted, and for years these had been producing about 35 per cent of the country's food on less than 3 per cent of its crop land. Indifferent to the collectivized fields and animals, the *kolkhozniks* lavished love and care on their private plots. It seemed apparent that one likely way to increase crops was to increase the size of the kitchen garden from the arbitrary half-acre maximum.

A broad public discussion of such issues was raised at the Third Kolkhoz Congress in 1967. Moreover, there were publicized suggestions for heavy increases in wholesale food prices to sharpen *kolkhoz* incentives and raise their members' incomes. There were demands for an increase in agricultural investments from the current 19 per cent of total investments to 26 per cent. Less widely publicized were suggestions to institute "team" responsibility, which would give control of farmland tracts to small groups of *kolkhozniks* for prolonged periods of time.

Official reaction has been cool, and it seems that Moscow leadership does not intend any such radical revision of the collective-farm system. Nor does it contemplate reintroduction of individual initiative or enterprise in agriculture or in the processing, packaging, marketing, and other interim operations, which had been taken over by the Soviet state and then largely ignored because heavy industry, military preparations, and world revolutionary activity had higher priorities. The reasons are both doctrinaire and pragmatic. The latter are probably the more important. The Party fears that it would lose control of the country's agriculture if it allowed a group of self-sufficient free farmers to begin operating, whether or not they had legal title to their land.

Agricultural policies and institutions are difficult to change in any society, and there is no indication that the Soviet Union is an exception. Prospects for change are even more remote in Mainland China.

The LDC's

The pattern of agriculture in the LDC's today is most diverse. True, feudalism and colonialism have all but disappeared under a variety of pressures, most important of which is probably the national liberation movements, which have produced scores of new nations in Asia and Africa during the past two decades. Most of these governments are inexperienced and far more interested in furthering their national prestige by maintaining international airlines and modern armies and building steel mills than they are in agriculture. Farming, in many minds, is still associated with the serfdom of yesteryear.

The result is the destruction of colonial and feudal institutions, along with economic operations that often had been productive over long periods of time. Javanese rubber plantations, for example, were operated for generations under the political and technical supervision of the Dutch. Although the Dutch may have retained inordinately large profits, they did use substantial sums to build cities, roads, schools, hospitals, and ports in Indonesia. After Sukarno took power from the Dutch, he became obsessed with leading the newly emerging forces to freedom and with his confrontation with Malaysia, and the rubber plantations fell into decay. As a result, in 1968 —years after Sukarno's overthrow and the creation of a more stable government—rubber production is still very low, and Indonesia's economy still probably in a state of net disinvestment.

India's maharajas were usually extravagant and exploitative, but they did furnish cohesive leadership to many states. Now almost all have disappeared, and in many cases the central government has not been able to put anything in their place. As a result, India's economy and its national homogeneity leave much to be desired.

Land reform would be useful in some parts of Latin America, but my interpretation is that in much of the continent "minifundia" is a greater problem than "latifundia." It is the consolidation of farms that are too small, rather than the breaking up of farms that are too large, which would vastly improve agricultural efficiency, although it might create other problems.

Throughout the LDC's the great need is for incentives, capital, a climate of security, and the education to motivate people to open up new farms and interim enterprises, and to run them with increased efficiency and productivity. But all too often impoverished and discouraged farmers, goaded by low food prices that their governments try to maintain for political reasons,* flock to the slum communities surrounding cities like Rio de Janeiro and Caracas, or simply crowd into cities such as Calcutta, where they sleep on the streets and try to live by any means they can.

When one travels through countries such as Brazil or Indonesia or India and sees hunger juxtaposed with unused resources and ostentatious consumption by the local rich, one is struck by the truth of the proposition that hunger is only one aspect—though a very important one—of the problem of poverty.

---

* While farmers want high food prices in order to make more money, urban consumers, whose voting power is substantial, would like low food prices in order to eat better. The governments of many countries feel it politically necessary to mollify the urban masses by maintaining low food prices.

Before proceeding with an analysis of measures that might effectively improve things, it is important to understand the diverse development patterns and vast food production changes that have taken place in the LDC's, the Communist states, and the developed market economies, as well as the geographic regions with which they more or less coincide.

For purposes of simplicity and clarity, consider two periods of time—the mid-1930's, and the mid-1960's—and seven broad geographic regions—North America (defined as Canada and the U.S.), Latin America (defined as all the rest of the Western Hemisphere), Western Europe, the Soviet Union and East Europe, Asia, Africa, and Oceania.

During the period between 1934 and 1938, the only one of these regions that maintained an average grain import position was Western Europe, which annually imported nearly 25 million tons. Where did it come from? The largest single supplier was Latin America, with annual average exports of just under ten million tons. Next in order came North America and the U.S.S.R.-East Europe region, each with average annual exports of five million tons. Oceania exported less than three million tons; Asia about two million tons; Africa less than one million.

Skipping over the horror and dislocation of World War II, let's look at the mid-1960's. Western Europe remains a heavy importer—about 23 million tons—but Asia, in the earlier period a small exporter, has now become far and away the heaviest importer—30 million tons. The Socialist states in Eastern Europe and the U.S.S.R. have now become importers of some 15 million tons, and Africa has moved from a modest supplier to a two-million-ton net importer. And where did this immense quantity of grain—70 million tons—come from? Sixty million tons of it came from North America. Latin America is still an exporter, but its shipments have fallen from nearly ten million tons to two million. Oceania has increased its shipments from two million tons to eight million.

These important figures are to be found in visual form in Appendix III.

Filling the Gap

There are several measures that would be useful in filling the gaps in the intricate chain connecting production and the hungry consumer.

First, extension services might be performed in many developed countries by ministries of agriculture. These go beyond soil analysis, fertilizer recommendations, and other problems immediately connected with the production of food. Such services already are generally available in the U.S., where the county agent acts as one channel of communication between the farmer and his market. Others are available to him through his cooperative and from farmer-beamed radio broadcasts on farm commodity prices and anticipated demands.

I visited a small farm near Madras, in southern India, where a former journalist colleague had withdrawn to the rural life. He was excited with his new crop—flowers. His land had always produced vegetables for the Madras market, but in the previous year he had stumbled onto some market gossip indicating that profits on flowers would be greater. He had taken the chance and had doubled his income in a single year. Delighted, he remarked, "Someone should have told me about this sooner. . . ." Indeed, throughout the LDC's lack of the kind of market information that every alert U.S. farmer hears on his radio before milking time each morning may inhibit increased productivity.

Whose responsibility should this be? The government radio networks in most of the LDC's are far more interested in propaganda and in more "important" political issues. In most LDC's, there are almost no rural or local private communications media trying to meet local farmers' needs. County agents in many LDC's are frightfully overworked and sometimes not well enough informed about local market conditions to fill this void in agricultural communications.

Improved harvesting is another step toward filling gaps in the production-consumption chain. This important operation is still carried out in most LDC's by hand or with the use of animal power—horses, water buffalo, oxen. But local manpower often is not available to harvest a crop quickly enough to plant the next crop. And when farmers are trying to double or triple crop their fields, this is of great importance. A mechanized mobile harvesting crew can frequently do the job much more rapidly, then move on to the next farm. Efficiency is improved, and the seasonal unemployment of local harvesting crews is reduced. Perhaps more important is the net saving in food, as draft animals require a large food input. Indeed, in Egypt, it is estimated that about one-third of the total food available in the country is consumed by the *gamooza,* or water buffalo. If either the small Japanese walk-behind tractor or the larger mechanized plowing and harvesting crew could be introduced, the food saving for the Egyptian economy would be much greater than the proportionate increase in food production that the Egyptians hope to realize from the Aswan High Dam. In parts of Southeast Asia this lesson has already been learned. In Thailand, for example, where a flexible free economy facilitates such developments, farmers have learned that the increase in yield and profits realized by custom crew ploughing and harvesting is far greater than the effort involved, and such entrepreneurs have sprung up, with positive results.

The transportation of the crop to market and availability of grain elevator or other central storage area is the next step. Here the importance of local "feeder" roads and of trucks or other transport vehicles is graphically apparent. Even the ancient ox cart can be modernized by the use of rubber tires, increasing efficiency by more than 100 per cent. Here the individual farmer often can do nothing directly, but the village or central government can, and in countries such as India, much has been done. An important aspect of India's "community development" program was the mobilization of idle local manpower in slack seasons to build local feeder roads. Similarly, in a project in northeastern Brazil such rural manpower was employed to build roads with materials supplied by the SUDENE, Brazil's TVA-like Superintendency for the Development of the Northeast. The workers were paid in PL 480 (U.S. AID) food imports, which were readily accepted, there being a scarcity in the area at the time.

Another example of inadequate transportation was observable in Madras. Visiting this southern Indian port, I noticed several vessels from which U.S. AID wheat was being unloaded. The work was unpleasant in the blazing heat. Dockworkers loaded the bulk grain into burlap bags, then slung the bags over their shoulders. They staggered up cleated planks to the dock, where the sacks were loaded onto ox carts for transfer to a central distribution point. The sacks were in poor repair, however, and grain constantly leaked onto the deck and the floor of the wharf. Inquiring why the sacks were not mended to save grain, I was told by the superintendent that I did not understand local conditions. It is a tradition that dockworkers get the sweepings at the end of the day. If there were no sweepings, a strike would occur in the morning. It is his function as superintendant to see that there are enough sweepings to avoid strikes but not so many as to spill into the sea.

It has been fairly reliably estimated that between one-quarter and one-third of all food available in India is consumed by pests—principally rats. One sound preventive measure would be to build cinderblock or concrete grain silos. But who is to do it? The Indian government has kept its public-sector investment resources for prestigious projects such as steel mills or military preparations, and has "allocated" the handling of food to the private sector. Yet, for understandable reasons, the government wants to maintain low retail food prices, while paying peasants as much as possible for their grain. Under these conditions, there is no motive for investment in grain elevators, and rats eat millions of tons of grain every year.

The Indian government must be persuaded to raise the priorities of the entire chain of food production and handling. Either it should allocate public-sector funds for grain elevators and flour mills, where many of the same inadequacies exist, or subsidize retail prices to permit the middleman a reasonable profit—or both.

Having mentioned prices, let us deal briefly with this important factor. In a classical free economy, prices are determined by supply and demand. However, this is today rare, for better or for worse. Even in the U.S., which often prides itself on being a "free" economy, the prices of principal agricultural commodities are subsidized by as much as several billion dollars a year by the Department of Agriculture. The same thing is true of Western Europe. Indeed, an excellent example of the leverage of agricultural prices is the Common Market. In the six member nations the farmers constitute only some 16 per cent of the population, but they are politically powerful enough

to have forced their governments to spend some $4.5 bil-
lion a year in price supports in 1968. The result was an
immense increase in agricultural stocks, including a substantial butter surplus that the Germans refer to as the
butterberg. Common Market Agricultural Chief Sicco
Manscholt responded in early 1969 by demanding a
drastic reduction in price supports, and even a $300 sub-
sidy for every cow slaughtered. Whether Manscholt's
demand is met or torpedoed by the powerful farm bloc,
the episode illustrates that price subsidies can be instrumental in increasing crops. A similar example is visible
in the 1968 crops in both India and Pakistan, where
scarcity prices left over from the two previous lean years
were instrumental in stimulating agricultural production.

In hard-pressed economies, prices are supplemented and
often eclipsed by rationing. In the Soviet Union in the
early 1930's, for instance, the price of free-market bread
was as much as tenfold the rationed price. India in 1967
is a more recent example of severe rationing and merits
more detailed discussion.

India Compared to Pakistan

During 1967 in India, grain was rationed at the rate of
one kilogram of wheat and one of rice per person per
week. Kerosene was also rationed. This rationing covered
7.3 million people in Calcutta and 1.2 million people
in seven adjacent industrial townships. Modified rationing, which provided 500 grams of rice and 1,300 grams of

wheat per week, embraced 14.7 million more. The remaining 24.5 million people of West Bengal, village peasants who lived very poorly, were not under rationing.

The procurement program for the government in Calcutta worked badly. The target was 1.5 million tons of rice by levy on the producers on the basis of their land holdings, but only about 550,000 tons were collected. The reason for this delinquency was that the big landholders did not cooperate. Free-market rice in Calcutta was about two and a half rupees per kilogram, or nearly three times the rationed price.

But Bengalis were learning to eat wheat. The rationed wheat cost about 45 paise* per kilogram, and on the market about three times as much. Hoarding by speculators was rampant in Calcutta. It was illegal, but because these speculators supported the Congress, they enjoyed immunity from prosecution.

In contrast to India, pricing in Pakistan was much more effectively handled. In Karachi, Harvard economist Dr. Richard Gilbert, who had served for seven years with the Pakistani government as adviser on economic development, offers the following explanation:

"Pakistan's agricultural production increased [during the 1950's] by an average of 1.3 per cent a year. However, the country was utterly swamped by the population growth, which averaged 2.4 per cent for the decade. Then, in 1959, the Pakistanis abolished price controls and re-

---

* One paise equals 1/100 rupee.

quisitions. . . . That was the first and most important step. We made it profitable and attractive to farm. We subsidized fertilizer by 50 per cent and pesticides almost entirely, and the use of both increased rapidly.

"In addition, we subsidized the drilling of tube wells and stimulated private entrepreneurs to start drilling and making simple diesel pumps. We are now drilling five wells in the private sector for every one drilled by the government. Over 2,000 wells have been drilled, utilizing the sweet water which underlies half of West Pakistan.

"By using incentives effectively, we achieved an average annual agricultural growth of 3.4 per cent during 1960–65. In 1966 the growth rate was about 5 per cent. In 1967 more than 5 per cent. The agricultural economy has reached the point of take-off."

During these same years, and until 1968, Indian government policy gave priorities to the public sector and discouraged private investment, both domestic and foreign. When prominent U.S. industrial and financial leaders tried to create a giant 1.2-million-ton fertilizer complex in India on a joint venture—$150 million to be invested by the U.S. consortium and a similar sum by the Indian government—middle-level Indian opposition torpedoed the project. The one large plant that was built, in Vizagaputnam by the International Minerals and Chemical Corporation of Skokie and the Chevron Oil Company of San Francisco, took eight years to construct, instead of the planned two, because of various obstructions.

The Pakistanis, on the other hand, encouraged both foreign and domestic investment and succeeded in increasing fertilizer production fivefold. They plan to be able to feed their population and to increase the average diet from the present 2,100 calories daily to 2,200 by 1970. The new varieties of wheat and rice will help them attain this goal.

The investment rate in Pakistan rose from 9.7 per cent of gross national product (GNP) in 1959–60 to 17.3 per cent in 1964–65. Exports increased by an average of 7 per cent a year. The proportion of national development expenditure in the private sector rose to 48 per cent. Although population growth increased during this period to about 3 per cent per year, other indices rose more rapidly. Pakistan was thus better off proportionately than during the previous decade in the production of food and industrial goods, and in the creation of new jobs.

The relative achievements of the Indians and Pakistanis are interesting to compare. The countries have similar backgrounds; their functionaries are largely the products of British education and training. The quality of most of the upper-level civil servants who staff the important ministries of both governments is impressive. Many of them are in their 40's or early 50's, dedicated and able administrators. They seem to have the balance and independence of professional functionaries who are relatively secure from political pressures. Many are assured of a fairly adequate pension at 55, usually supplementable by teaching or advising. In neither country, however, do these men set policy; this is done in India by the Prime Minister and the cabinet, and in Pakistan by the President. But in both countries the regional administration of policy is left in the hands of the vast and frequently inefficient apparatus of lower-level civil servants.

The system was created by the British, and it was designed essentially to prevent rebellious action. Now, both governments want to initiate spirited action but are saddled with an administrative apparatus created for the opposite purpose. The situation is particularly evident in India, where, despite the presence of many highly qualified officials, policies are often somewhat unrealistic and implementation is imperfect.

Interestingly, India started out in a stronger position. She had more industry than Pakistan, whose bifurcated territory was difficult to administer. But the Pakistanis have made better use of their human and material resources in the past two decades. They now have a per capita GNP of about $90 U.S., compared to India's $60, and the Pakistanis are both relatively and absolutely less dependent on foreign aid.

A decisive difference between the two countries is perhaps the Indian tendency to theorize rather than act. Also influential is the Indian caste tradition, still doggedly present, which makes educated Indians tend to avoid physical work and direct action in favor of issuing directives to others.

Another important factor is that Indian leadership, partially for religious reasons, has tended to view private enterprise as essentially evil, whereas Pakistani leadership tends to regard it as a constructive tool in economic development. Thus, whereas the Indians have built monumental steel mills and other symbols of public-sector heavy industrialization, the Pakistanis have concentrated on private-sector agricultural and industrial development, more modest, but so far, more effective.

Other Factors

Other efforts to improve the production of food and its flow to the consumer include the areas of processing and packaging. In much of the developing world, processing is limited to crude milling, and packaging is not done at all. In many rural stores, wheat, beans, and other foods are displayed in bulk and when sold are weighed and wrapped —usually in sacks or old newspaper—for each customer. Indeed, until the 1960's the same thing was true in the Soviet Union. In most LDC's there is little processing such as the manufacture of macaroni, cheese, crackers, cakes, or pies, and precooked frozen foods such as those available in U.S. supermarkets are scarcely seen. The development of these products requires capital, as well as a public able to afford such luxuries. Neither is currently present in the LDC's.

As mentioned in the section on nutrition, a more sophisticated aspect of food processing is fortification of ordinary foods such as flour or oatmeal with protein concentrates and vitamins. This has just been started in the LDC's, although such products as Incaparina and protein colas have been introduced and are doing rather well in some specialized markets. This kind of processing has great potential and was discussed more fully in Chapter VI.

Finally, orderly and effective movement of food from producer to consumer requires effective management. It is painfully discouraging to find hunger side by side with food reserves whose distribution and use has been inhibited essentially by the lack of competent management.

Of course, one does not have to go to the LDC's to find these phenomena. Children are suffering from malnutrition in New York City today—tens of thousands of them —though there is no shortage of food.

But there seems to be a greater number of poignant examples in the LDC's. A colleague and I were traveling in northeastern Brazil and decided to visit the town of Patos in the state of Paraíba where, some reports said, people were starving. Soon after landing on the grass-and-gravel strip, we met a local cotton farmer, who informed us that there was enough water for 60 days, and then the cattle would begin to die. His cotton was in poor shape, and he was extremely worried about the hundred families on his farm.

Driving through the countryside, we visited a road construction job, where about 2,800 men, unemployed because of the drought, were building a simple dirt road using only hand tools and wheelbarrows. They were poorly dressed, but seemed to be well enough fed to have normal reflexes and to do hard work. The children, however, looked definitely undernourished. Wages were paid half in food and half in money from emergency state funds. We were told that as soon as it rained, the workers would return to their farms, and the road job would be left half finished. "These droughts are bad for agriculture, but they are good for the infrastructure," remarked a local functionary.

In the Patos marketplace we saw tons of food at prices below those of Rio: shelled corn at about three U.S. cents a pound, rice at about twice that, manioc flour at about seven cents. Meat was plentiful, too, but at prices too high for the very poor—about 45 cents a pound.

Patos was one of the most drought-ridden towns in the northeast, Brazil's poorest region. Yet food was available. The problem here was essentially poverty, rather than an inadequate food supply. As I stood in the Patos market, I realized that only rarely and under extraordinary circumstances, such as the siege of Leningrad, the famine in Bengal in 1943, or the man-made famine in the Ukraine in the 1930's, does mass starvation occur because of lack of food. In most cases hunger is an aspect of poverty. Children suffer the disorders of malnutrition usually not because food is unavailable, but because their parents cannot buy what is there.

One requirement for an effective approach to these shortcomings of food production and distribution is education for all levels of the population. What of countries that lack educated specialists and cannot expect soon to fill this need? It takes years to train an agronomist, geneticist, or economic planner.

To what extent is it advisable for the U.S. to press its LDC friends to adopt new agricultural techniques, to make structural revisions and institutional and political modifications that would hasten the day of self-sufficiency in food? Conditions vary from country to country, of course. Often technical suggestions are accepted by the governments of the LDC's and produce results, as was the case with recommendations for large numbers of private-sector tube wells in West Pakistan. Similar suggestions were quietly ignored by Indian officials. There are, however, severe limits on what one nation can compel other nations to do.

I believe that U.S. officials might insist on technical and structural reforms only in cases where the country involved is a heavy recipient of direct public-sector aid. Such procedures are understood, if not always accepted, on a smaller scale in the U.S. and even in the Soviet economy. When a plant director in either country requests a bank loan to make improvements, the bank asks for and gets detailed information about the enterprise. The bank often grants the loan only on condition that certain technical or organizational changes be made. If the loan is a large one, the bank frequently puts a man on the recipient's board. In this context, I think the U.S. can and should use its position as the world's largest granary nation to accelerate the modernization not only of agricultural techniques in the LDC's, but of the entire structure of their food economies.

If such measures are taken, world food production may

increase by 4 per cent a year during the next generation—
the rate needed to feed the world's hungry in the years
immediately ahead.

What organizational framework is best adapted to effect
these measures? What instruments of persuasion and en-
couragement are best calculated to achieve the modernization of the food economies of the LDC's without injuring
their sensitive national egos? And—at the same time—
what organizations want to attempt this difficult task?

Food Around the World

87. *Enough food for everyone—the goal.*

88. *Indian woman in Dutch Guiana carries basket of yams.*

89. *Husking cocoanuts for the Copra industry in Malaysia.*

90. *Market scene in Nasik, India, provides glimpse of food there and the "holy" cows.*

91. *In Sumatra, Indonesia, the Brastagi market sells dureans and mangostems.*

92. *Ceylonese tea pickers. Tea is chief export of Ceylon.*

93. Noodles? Guess again.
Kounafa, *eaten during*
Egypt's festival of Ramadan.

94. Dried vegetables and grains
on display at this Turkish
market in the Anatolian Plains.

95. Meat in a Cairo
"open air" shop.

96. *This little girl of Transkei, Cape Province, South Africa, uses her head to get melons to market.*

97. *Date market in Biskra, Algeria. Date seeds can be roasted as substitute for coffee.*

98. *In the Congo, roast chicken with native pepper is a treat.*

99. *Biafran women prepare yams, a food widely used in their country, when available.*

100. *Women in a Japanese noodle shop prepare for a light snack or lunch.*

101. *Supper time in Korea . . .*

102.   *. . . and also in Shanghai, China.*

103. This "backer" catches the bananas as they are cut in Honduras.

104. Brazilian fruit boat unloads at Belern on the Amazon River.

105. No tears as these Mexican children of Cuidad del Maiz clean onions.

106. Cutting the cactus near Vera Cruz, which is used to make mescal and tequila, traditional Mexican drinks.

107. "To market, to market" . . . Indian in Ecuador takes chicken to be sold.

108. *Potential pork chops on a Kansas farm.*

109. *Government meat inspection in Norfolk, Virginia.*

110. *Beans is the fare in this Tennessee household.*

111. German pretzel stand at Munich's annual Octoberfest.

112. Danish butter being weighed.

113. Shaping mozzarella, the famous Italian cheese.

114. Watermelons for sale at Sarajevo, Yugoslavia.

115. French cheese market in Normandy.

116. Picking grapes for French wine.

117. Supper? Oui.

11 Bridging the Gap

THE LDC'S HAVE only about 20 per cent as much arable land per farmer as do the developed countries. In 1960 the developed countries had a 115-million farm population with 37 million hectares of arable land at its disposal—or 3.22 hectares per farmer. In the LDC's, a 920-million farm population had 680 million hectares, or 0.74 per farmer.

Levels of food availability and intake also vary radically. In the years 1957–61, North America's yearly per capita production of grain was 1,057 kilograms—nearly twice as much as those of Eastern Europe and the U.S.S.R., at 541, or Oceania at 533. Latin America, Asia, and Africa all stood below 225. After deducting exports from North America and Oceania and adding imports to the developing areas, the grain available for consumption per person was 883 kilograms for North America, 542 for the Soviet bloc, 364 for Western Europe, 230 for Asia, 207 for Latin America, and 171 for Africa.

How do North Americans consume nearly six pounds of grain per person each day? By feeding it to chickens, cattle, and hogs and eating the meat and dairy products— higher in protein, more concentrated, and more tasty, but also much more expensive. How do Africans get along on less than a pound of grain a day? Their poor diets usually leave them de-energized, harassed by diseases of malnutrition, their children listless and retarded.

During the past 25 years North American yields have increased by an average of 3 per cent a year, compounded annually; in Asia the average yield increase has been 0.3 per cent a year. One cause of this ten-to-one difference is greater expenditures on agricultural research, which governments of developed countries have been able to afford. A sampling of government research budgets per farmer per year in U.S. dollars is as follows:

India 0.05	Taiwan 0.49
Thailand 0.05	Japan 0.69
Philippines 0.27	U.S. 45.90
Mexico 0.35	

In view of these discrepancies, it is not surprising that the Presidential National Advisory Commission on Foods and Fibers reports that "one billion people in the developed countries eat half again as many calories and five times as much high-quality protein per person" as the two billion people in the LDC's.

Governments and people of the LDC's are often partially responsible for their situation. However, one should remember that countries such as India are trying to nourish some 14 per cent of the world's population on about 2 per cent of its resources.

What Is Required to Convert
"Need" into "Demand"?

Development is the major framework within which national and international organizations, private voluntary groups, and individuals can measure their successes and failures in helping the LDC's. Two examples of formerly underdeveloped countries that have used a substantial quantity of both public and private aid to reach the economic "take-off " point within a very few years are Taiwan and Israel. Both now are able to buy what they need from overseas and pay for most of it in convertible currency. Both became sovereign nations at approximately the same time—1949. Both inherited some infrastructure—roads, schools, ports—from the Japanese and the British respectively, but not nearly enough industry or other assets to be self-sufficient.

Between 1950 and 1965, about $1.5 billion in non-military aid went from the U.S. to Taiwan, largely in the public sector. When the program started, the Taiwanese economy was badly dislocated by the war and by the

invasion of nearly one million Mainlanders—the administration and army of the Chinese Nationalists—whose presence sparked serious and bloody conflicts. But thanks to
outside aid, to Taiwanese work, and to Chiang Kai-shek's
stable government, progress was made:

The GNP increased by more than 7 per cent per year,
on the average.

Farm production increased by some 4.5 per cent per
year, and yields doubled.

Industrial production increased by some 13 per cent per
year, on the average.

Per capita income increased by about 3.5 per cent per
year in real terms.

Exports increased some sixfold.

By 1965 Taiwan had reached the economic take-off
point and was beginning to extend economic aid to others
—modest programs to nineteen African and two Asian
countries involving some 600 technicians and a budget of
about $4 million.

In 1965 the U.S. economic aid program to Taiwan was
discontinued as having fulfilled its objectives, and since
then the economy has continued to grow vigorously. During the 15 years of its existence, the AID program delivered a total of about $100 million per year, or an aver-
age of about $10 per person per year. (The population of
Taiwan is now about 13 million, but the average over the
15 years was 10 million.) This per capita figure seems to
be the amount of outside economic aid required to put a
country on its feet.

It is interesting to note that if this principle is applied to Mainland China with its perhaps 750 million population, the inputs of capital required to bring the economy to the take-off point would be some $7.5 billion a year for 15 years. There is not even half that much in all the world's aid budgets.

Another country in which aid was effectively used is Israel, although conditions were far different. Israel received some public-sector aid, but far more came on a voluntary basis from Jewish funds throughout the world. The sum was about $250 million a year for the past 15 years, and Israel's average population over that period of time was about two million, equaling more than $100 a year per person, or ten times what Taiwan received. The country, however, is far less lush than Taiwan, and many of its immigrants had to be taught skills and the language of the land. Furthermore, Israel's continuing battle with its Arab neighbors has been a developmental drawback. But despite these difficulties and expenditures, the economy made remarkable progress. In 1955 outside aid comprised more than one-third of the Israeli GNP; in 1969 it made up only 12 per cent. Exports have not only increased, but consist in great measure of the products of brand-new industries such as poultry, machine tools, aircraft components, electronics. Israeli food production increased manyfold; in many formerly arid areas, the desert blooms. And, like Taiwan, Israel has also initiated an impressive aid program of its own.

Most LDC's, however, cannot even dream of comparable outside economic resources, and very few nations in the past hundred years have achieved the take-off point without at least some outside aid or investment. United States industry was built largely with European capital, and much of the work was done by slaves imported from Africa and by laborers imported from Europe and Asia during the years before World War I.

Let us now examine the various organizations currently trying to help the LDC's feed themselves.

The FAO

The U.N. Food and Agriculture Organization, which is headquartered in Rome, is perhaps the best starting point because of its broad base and the wide scope of its operations.

Although the FAO is a part of the United Nations, not all of its members belong to the U.N. For example, West Germany, although not in the U.N., is a member and indeed the second-largest contributor to the FAO. The Soviet Union, on the other hand, has never joined the FAO. The FAO has 2,300 full-time employes in Rome, 1,700 elsewhere. Its budget is about $25 million a year, but it administers more than $100 million of U.N. and other development funds.

The principal contributors to the FAO—the U.S. (which alone supplies nearly one-third of its budget), Germany, Great Britain, and France—in that order—pay more than half the bills and have considerable influence

with Director General A. H. Boerma, former director of
the FAO World Food Program and onetime Minister of
Food in his native Holland.

Mention of several functionaries illustrates the variety
of FAO's activities: M. L. Goreaux, an internationalized
Frenchman, who worked on the Indicative World Plan, a
partially completed project whose purpose is to put pertinent data into a computer system capable of indicating optimal priorities for FAO efforts in various fields. Roy Jack-
son of the Fisheries Department has at his fingertips the
essential information on production and development of
fish and shellfish in the world's oceans and inland waters.
Vladimir Ignatieff of the Land and Water Division works
with irrigation in both specific and long-term objectives.

Oris Wells, a former official of the U.S. Department of
Agriculture, is now Deputy Director General of FAO.
Under his direction, the FAO has achieved the fundamental change from a statistics-gathering bureau into an
operating agency with projects and programs in many
parts of the world. The U.S. Department of Agriculture
underwent a similar change—between the Hoover and
the second Roosevelt administrations—but there is one
important difference between the operations of the FAO
and those of the U.S. Department of Agriculture. In certain areas—acreage allotments and price supports, for example—the Department of Agriculture can order; the
FAO can only recommend. It can send its personnel to
member countries only when requested to do so. This

makes it necessary for the FAO to combine diplomacy with agricultural technology and economics in the context of the vastly different traditions and mores of member states.

The World Food Program commenced in 1963 with the basic philosophy that food is not just something to eat, but is seed capital. The idea was to use food to launch needed projects in the less-developed countries, working with the unemployed and with contributed materials. There are now 350 approved projects in 80 countries. South Korea is a graphic example. The 10,000-acre portion of land selected was rocky, eroded, and divided into two- or three-acre subsistence farms. The farmers were impoverished and unproductive.

The World Food Program claims to have fed several thousand farmers and otherwise unemployed farm laborers, and the Korean government matched the value of this food with money paid as wages to those who worked at grading, leveling, erosion control, and irrigation. In less than two years, production doubled. Now the government of Korea wants to do the same thing with another 100,000 acres.

From where does the food come? It is contributed from other countries, largely by the U.S. Contributions total about $70 million worth yearly. Food is shipped to the port of entry of the recipient country, which then must handle and distribute it under WFP supervision. Most of the projects run two to four years, and each must have a beginning and an end so that something tangible can be created. In the first three years FAO fed one million people, including 233,000 settlers and 100,000 schoolchildren, and put 350,000 men to work on useful projects.

The Operations Liaison Branch of the FAO has 107 missions around the world attempting to act as an international extension service. The Fertilizer Program has some 1,700 full- or part-time field workers conducting nearly 20,000 demonstrations yearly for farmers in 83 countries. Other divisions of FAO are the Freedom from Hunger Program, the Wildlife Division, the Plant Disease and Livestock divisions, and several reporting divisions that draft and edit volumes of literature on all aspects of world food problems in many languages.

At any given time, there are perhaps 500 individual expert missions at work all over the world. An example is Afghanistan, where only one child in five is in school. Here, the World Food Program, jointly with other agencies and the Afghani government, has organized a program providing $1.6 million worth of wheat, dried milk, canned meat, and other foods for students who attend district schools, sometimes many miles from their homes. The World Food Program also supplies and operates the cafeterias at the Kabul Institute of Technology and Kabul University.

As one might expect, FAO cooperates with organizations whose areas of activity overlap. The United Nations Childrens' Fund, UNICEF, for example, engages in some projects jointly with FAO. The World Bank and its regional branches are also in constant contact with the

FAO. One of the most important organizations, many of whose activities are carried out by and through the FAO, is the United Nations Development Program, or UNDP, which is administered by Paul Hoffman. The UNDP was formed by a merger of the U.N. Expanded Program of Technical Assistance and the United Nations Special Fund. Funds for the UNDP come in both hard and soft currencies from U.N. members in roughly the same proportion as their U.N. dues. Projects are selected by the administrator in consultation with an interagency board consisting of the U.N. Secretary-General and the top leadership of specialized U.N. agencies such as FAO, ILO, and others. In general, the projects must be initiated by the government of the country on whose territory the work is to be done and must be aimed at helping that country toward self-sufficiency. The requesting governments are expected to meet some of the administrative expenses of feasibility studies of UNDP projects and to furnish some local personnel and counterpart funds in local currencies to help maintain the outside technical personnel. During each of the past several years the FAO has administered some $40 million a year of UNDP funds in more than 300 projects all over the world.

Critics of the FAO accuse it of being too large and describe its many "experts" as "an arbitrary collection of fundamentally incompetent persons coming from all parts of the world to undertake surveys of countries unknown to them." It is true that any large international bureaucracy—particularly one with the broad mission of helping a hungry world produce planned surpluses of food—is prone to administrative proliferation. Yet, in the final analysis, the achievements of FAO undoubtedly far outweigh its shortcomings.

The World Bank and its Affiliates

The international development banks have been important in making basic surveys and in initiating and supporting sound economic development projects all over the world. By extending both 15- and 20-year loans at commercial rates and 50-year credits interest-free (International Development Association credits), these banks have provided vital support to projects involving food and agriculture, transportation, power, land, conservation, education, and industrial development.

Known formerly as the International Bank for Reconstruction and Development, the World Bank is headed by Robert S. McNamara. It has 107 members and a total subscribed capital of $22.9 billion. With current reserves of $1,160 million, the bank makes loans of some $800 million annually.

In some respects, the World Bank functions like an ordinary commercial bank. It raises money by subscription and by selling bonds and loans; it tries to lend its money wisely and to avoid defaults on loans. It has been notably successful. In 1968 the bank had a net income of $169 million, almost exactly the same as in the previous year. Its administrative expenses for the year aggregated a modest $29 million. Besides making loans, the World Bank cooperates with such organizations as the International Monetary Fund in studying problems most important for the LDC's—the stabilization of primary commodity prices, the realization of regional programs such as the Mekong River Valley Development, and such world problems as population control. Plans for future bank activities include an expansion of loans to the billion-dollar level during the years immediately ahead.

Several regional banks that cooperate with the World Bank have undertaken similar functions. These include the Inter-American Development Bank, the African Development Bank, and the Asian Development Bank. The Asian bank, which opened in Manila in January 1967, began with a subscribed capital of $1 billion, of which Japan and the U.S. each contributed $200 million. The current president of the institution is a Japanese banker, Takeshi Watanabe. A major project undertaken by the Asian Development Bank was a survey of Asian food production.

The list of purposes for which the World Bank and its regional affiliates have lent money makes clear the importance of food in the banks' activities. A selection taken from the most recent list of loans to 31 countries includes: Argentina, livestock development; Brazil, livestock production; Ceylon, irrigation; Costa Rica, agricultural credit; Iran, irrigation and land development; Kenya, tea production; Malawi, land development; Malaysia, land settlement; Mexico, irrigation; Pakistan, agricultural credit; and so on. The interest rates at which all of these banks lend money is contingent upon the interest that the bank itself must pay. During the past several years the rates have varied between 5½ and 7 per cent.

To Further Regional Cooperation

Cooperating with these banks in initiating and implementing development projects in the LDC's are a galaxy of regional organizations—some associated with the United Nations, others independent. To cite just one that is active in East Asia, ECAFE—the Economic Commission for Asia and the Far East—is a regional organization of the United Nations with headquarters in Bangkok. Its members include nations whose shores are washed by the western Pacific plus the Soviet Union, the United States, Canada, France, the United Kingdom, the Netherlands, Pakistan, India, and Iran, for a total of 27. The ECAFE sponsors other specialized organizations, such as SEAMES —the Southeast Asian Ministers of Education Secretariat, ASEAN—the Association of Southeast Asian Nations, APC—the Asia and Pacific Council, APO—the Asian Productivity Organization, and the Council of Southeast Asian Officials on Transport and Communications.

The meetings of these organizations are frequently stormy, for long-standing territorial disputes are hard to overcome. Harmony is impeded by the unsolved conflict between the Philippine Republic and Malaysia over Brunei in Northern Borneo, the ancient rivalries between Thailand and Burma, the fears of Cambodia's President Sihanouk that his territory will be violated, and until recently, Sukarno's "confrontation" with Malaysia. These sovereign nations, however, whose populations total nearly half a billion, have made significant progress. All were under Chinese suzerainty for centuries, and later (except for Thailand) were colonies of European powers for many generations. All felt the impact of Japanese power during World War II, and all now are intensely conscious and proud of their national sovereignty. That these nations are now actively engaged in a variety of multinational organizations aimed at the cooperative solution of their many common problems—the most important of which is food—is an undeniable accomplishment.

U.S. AID

In proportion to its GNP, the U.S. ranks only seventh in the world in giving economic aid to LDC's. Portugal and France, for example, both give more aid per dollar of their own income. However, because the U.S. is so productive by an absolute measure, its aid program over recent years has been far greater in quantity, if not percentage, than that of the other countries combined. The U.S.S.R., however, is a close second to the U.S. In 1966, the U.S. was the greatest contributor to the spectacular emergency aid to India, and it has consistently made immense contributions, both in actual food and in technical assistance, fertilizers, and ancillary projects such as feeder roads, irrigation canals, technical high schools, medical projects, and the training of large numbers of young people from the LDC's on scholarships in varied educational institutions in the United States.

Much of the U.S. aid effort—about $59 billion worth—was made in loans and grants immediately after World War II to rehabilitate both its allies and its defeated enemies in Europe and Asia. The focus of this book, however, is on food. Therefore, we shall discuss U.S. aid in terms of shipments of actual food and of aid projects designed to help the hungry nations feed themselves.

In 1954, Public Law 480 was first passed. It had several sections or titles. Under certain circumstances it authorized the shipment of U.S. grain and other foods to needy nations as outright gifts. Under other circumstances the food was to be paid for in local currency, which thereby became so-called counterpart funds. This money belonged to the United States, but it could be used only in the recipient country and was to be expended for secondary aid projects such as financing local small businessmen in transportation or food-processing industries. In some cases, the counterpart funds could be used within the country for U.S. government purposes, such as the building of embassy buildings or the meeting of operational expenditures of U.S. organizations.

The PL-480 program was begun only in 1955, when less than $1 billion was sent as aid, plus $2.3 billion sold, a total of more than $3 billion in exports. The shipments increased unevenly until, in 1962, the exports reached $1.5 billion under PL-480, plus $3.6 billion in commercial sales, or a total of more than $5 billion. By 1966 the figures had risen to $1.6 billion in aid and $5.1 billion in sales, or a total of $6.7 billion. The cumulative total of aid and sales from 1955 to 1966 was $57 billion, of which $17 billion was aid.

The 1966 deliveries showed wheat and wheat flour to be the most important single item, but substantial quantities of oilseeds and oilseed products, cotton, feed grains, dairy products, and tobacco were also shipped. Since 1966 the law has been changed, and the "Food for Peace" legislation of 1967 provides for smaller shipments to be paid for eventually in hard currency over long periods of time—20 to 25 years—at 1 per cent interest. Currently, shipments have leveled off at about $1.5 billion a year, largely because the massive shipments of 1967 depleted U.S. grain reserves. Because the change in the law did not take place earlier, instead of being owed dollars, the U.S. now finds itself in the embarrassing position of owning almost half the Indian currency in circulation.

An interesting aspect of these huge grain shipments is their intimate relationship with U.S. agricultural price supports and acreage allotments. If the U.S. were to cut grain shipments when the receiver could not pay, it would have to reduce domestic production (after building up reserves to the optimal minimum level of about a two-year supply). But according to experts in the Department of Agriculture, since the U.S. does not want to see farm incomes reduced, the cost in subsidies of *not* producing a bushel of corn is about $1.03, whereas the price paid for it after it is produced is only $1.09. Thus, the cost of maintaining Food for Peace shipments to the LDC's is not nearly so large as it might seem.

Another consideration involved in large shipments of food to the LDC's is that the recipient nation sometimes obtains free, or on long-term credit, what it would otherwise have to buy, and such grain receipts tend to depress local food prices. As has been previously mentioned, local food production tends to be stimulated by high food prices. The farmers get more for their crop and try to grow bigger crops. Conversely, when prices fall, they are discouraged, and grow only that which each needs for himself and his family; some go to town to get factory jobs, thereby further reducing the country's food production. Thus, under certain conditions food aid to LDC's can reduce rather than increase the country's ability to take care of itself.

Other kinds of U.S. aid to the LDC's include such diverse projects as land reclamation in the Dominican Republic, development of farm products marketing in Bolivia, an agricultural statistics service in Chile, a market news system and a price stabilization program in Brazil, agricultural credit and pest control programs in El Salvador, a plant protection program in Ethiopia, an agricultural credit program in Nigeria, soil conservation projects in Tunisia, introduction of new grains in India, and an ambitious assortment of agricultural projects in South Vietnam. In many LDC's the U.S. Department of Agriculture carries out a wide range of research projects involving agricultural techniques and nutrition, which at least indirectly are part of the complex chain of feeding the hungry.

Assistance alone, however, is not enough to make individuals willing and able to help themselves. Essentially, each must be convinced of four things before the complex chemistry of development aid can work effectively:

First, each must know that the new practices he is offered—fertilizers, new varieties, pesticides, double and triple cropping, mechanization—can and do work.

Second, each must learn to use these so that he can do so independently.

Third, each must see that needed materials—seeds, fertilizers, credits—are available at acceptable prices.

Finally, each must believe that if he does increase his crop substantially there will be a market and acceptable prices for his products.

To accomplish these things is the over-all objective of the aid program. Accomplishing only part is often of no use at all, but attempting to meet such goals often taxes the patience and ingenuity of the most skillful officials.

In 1968 Congress cut U.S. AID funds heavily, leaving them at only $1.8 billion, the lowest since U.S. AID began. These U.S. cuts result from balance-of-payments difficulties, from high expenditures for the war in Vietnam, and from diminishing favorable trade balance caused by U.S. inflation. In 1958, however, the total U.S. economic aid to all countries was probably just a bit smaller than the total economic aid of the U.S.S.R. Given that the

U.S. GNP is more than twice that of the Russians, the U.S. is giving far less proportionately than they.

An important final aspect of foreign aid is the cumulative burden of debt that it imposes on the recipient LDC's. Of the grand total of $117 billion in aid that went from the U.S. to other countries between 1945 and 1968, about 30 per cent went to the LDC's. Food shipments totaled about $17 billion, almost none of which had to be repaid immediately in hard currency; but for other kinds of shipments, the LDC's involved themselves in debts that now require constant servicing, and they often have to borrow more money to make interest payments. Payments cannot be made from current income from exports because of the deterioration of the terms of trade—the gradual decline in prices of primary commodities exported by the LDC's, such as coffee, cocoa, ores, and petroleum, and the gradual increase in prices of manufactured goods such as automobiles and tractors that they import. The result of this squeeze is seen in the fact that the estimated medium- and long-term debts of the developed countries stood at $14 billion in 1956 and rose to $16.6 billion in 1967, whereas the medium- and long-term debts of the LDC's stood at $9.7 billion in 1956 and grew to $41 billion by 1967. Thus, an estimated 44 per cent of all aid flowing in 1966 from developed countries to the LDC's went to pay interest. To cite several specific examples: In 1966 the following countries had to pay the indicated percentages of their total exports as interest on foreign debts and profits on foreign investments: Brazil, 13.8 per cent; Chile, 19.8 per cent; Pakistan, 10.1 per cent; India, 15.6 per cent; Mexico, 30.4 per cent; Turkey, 20.3 per cent; Venezuela, 26.1 per cent. The unpleasant political consequences of this situation are obvious. Only those LDC's that have managed to maintain very high economic growth rates, such as Mexico and Pakistan, are able to keep their heads above water. Others are almost certain to sink gradually into hopeless penury unless saved by massive debt moratoriums or unilateral nationalization and debt repudiation.

Private Sector Organizations That Care

There are a number of helping organizations in the private sector. Some are foundations with philanthropic or political motives; some are religious, seeking both to proselytize and to help their less fortunate brothers; and some are businesses seeking to develop the resources of the LDC's and to make a profit in doing so.

More than 500 nonprofit voluntary organizations in the U.S. work in various ways to assist the LDC's, spending some $750 million annually on their activities, and enjoying various degrees of tax exemption. Dozens have made contributions in the fields of nutrition and production of food. Two of the largest and most successful of these organizations are the Rockefeller and Ford foundations.

The Rockefeller Foundation was formed in 1913 to "promote the well-being of mankind throughout the world." The Ford Foundation was organized much later, in 1950, but since then it has made grants totaling more than $1.5 billion and has become the world's largest philanthropic organization.

Let us look at several concrete examples of their achievements. In 1941 the late Henry A. Wallace, then U.S. Vice President, suggested to the Rockefeller Foundation that it devote attention to improving yields of the corn and beans that constitute the staple food of most Mexicans. Until that point, most of the foundation's work had been in the areas of medicine and public health.

Using the hybrid varieties of corn developed during the 1930's, partly by Wallace, his father, and their associates in Iowa, the foundation went to work. New varieties of corn were developed—types adapted to Mexican conditions and resistant to local diseases. By 1948 the average yield of Mexico's cornfields had risen from eight bushels per acre in 1941, to a figure approaching the U.S. average of 35 bushels per acre. Mexico found itself self-sufficient in corn for the first time since the Revolution of 1910. Shortly thereafter, the Rockefeller Foundation began work on wheat, attempting to develop a rust-resistant variety with a short stiff stem, capable of absorbing large inputs of fertilizer and water without lodging. It is this work that has borne such rewarding fruit in the past several years in the new wheats such as Mexipak.

Since rice is the most important single source of food for man, it was natural that the foundations turn their attention in that direction. In 1962 the Rockefeller and Ford foundations jointly established the International

Rice Research Institute (I.R.R.I.) in the Philippine Republic. The initial grant was only $5 million each, but the results achieved have already been worth hundreds of times that sum for the hungry. Not only has the I.R.R.I. developed a number of rice varieties that mature in 120 days and increase yield per acre severalfold, it has also trained hundreds of specialists from many countries who have helped introduce the new varieties into fields around the world. A total of 104 specialists from 19 countries received such training in 1966 alone.

In the early 1950's the Ford Foundation initiated a project in India that was to have far-reaching effects. Known as the Community Development Program, it was aimed at helping villagers use their local resources and labor power to dig wells, build schools, improve local roads, and increase crop production. Community Development teams work in rural India, introducing new ideas and helping young villagers to overcome cumulative inertia, and to improve their lot. The Ford Foundation also launched the International Institute of Tropical Research in Ibadan, Nigeria, which has made major contributions to agricultural and nutritional improvements in Africa.

Many other foundations have done effective work, among them the Kellogg Foundation, which founded the Central American Institute of Nutrition. Organizations such as the Planned Parenthood Federation and the Population Council have been able to do their work largely on foundation grants. The foundations have also cooperated with a number of religious groups such as the Church

World Service, the Catholic Relief Service, the American Friends' Service Committee, the Jewish Joint Distribution Committee, and many others. One of the most effective of these groups is the Cooperative for American Relief Everywhere—CARE. Set up in 1945 and financed by diverse sources, CARE has fed millions of hungry people all over the world.

Hundreds of other volunteer groups have helped fight hunger, including the U.S.-sponsored voluntary organization, the Peace Corps.

Private Investment

Private investors are, by definition, essentially interested in making a profit, but they sometimes are willing to work hard over long periods to build something that will eventually become profitable. Of the roughly $60 billion in direct U.S. private investments all over the world, more than two-thirds is in developed countries—namely Canada and Western Europe. Furthermore, a large part of the investments made in the LDC's has been in the extractive industries, principally petroleum and metal ores, and in industrial crops such as rubber in Liberia. However, several billion dollars in private investment has gone into fertilizer plants, tea plantations, cattle ranches, and other projects connected with the struggle against hunger.

For instance, when the United Fruit Company became active in Central America three generations ago, they had to start with the most basic steps to develop the fruit potential of these tropical countries. They had to build their own railroads and roads, drain and clear land, build schools and clinics, and train local personnel in everything from hydraulic engineering to microbiology. Like the South Puerto Rican Sugar Company, the Firestone Rubber Company in Liberia, and sugar and fruit companies active in Hawaii and the Philippines, their objective was clearly to make money. Profits were indeed made and plowed back into the enterprises or repatriated as dividends to the investors. This often aroused the antagonism of the native people, who felt they were being exploited, and exploited they were. But along with exploitation came development and opportunities that otherwise would not have been available. Thus, de facto, private capital did contribute to development of local food resources and make available new opportunities for local people.

As another instance, the International Minerals and Chemical Corporation of Skokie, Illinois, the Chevron Oil Company of San Francisco, and the Indian government jointly built a fertilizer plant in Visakhapatnam, in east India. The American investors put in $80 million and spent nearly eight years building a plant that could have been constructed and commissioned in a quarter of the time in a developed country where materials were more readily available and red tape was less abundant. In 1968 the plant began to make a modest profit. The output of 360,000 tons of ammonium sulphate a year—nearly as much as India's total production when the construction began—will probably improve yields of India's food crops. The company has trained a corps of salesmen-technicians who travel around teaching farmers to use fertilizer to its maximum effect. Here again, private investment has helped development and has fed the hungry, while concurrently making a profit.

In my opinion, wide utilization of private investment to help the LDC's solve their food problems is preferable to government aid, which must be supplied by the taxpayers of developed nations. Because of national pride, however, and a fear of finding themselves permanently enslaved by exploitative foreign companies, the LDC's often resist private investment in equity ownership. Fortunately, some methods have been devised through which the initiative and technical know-how of private companies can be made available to develop new economies while avoiding political unpopularity and possible eventual confiscation or nationalization of plants and plantations built.

The most fundamental method is the joint venture—the enterprise organized by foreign and local investors or companies, sometimes in cooperation with the local government. The purpose is to build a plant using local materials and manpower and foreign technology, manufacturing, and marketing experience for the joint benefit of everyone concerned. Often such ventures have foundered when foreign specialists insisted on being in charge of the plant because "we know the business and they don't." Understandably, the local people desire managerial responsibility, but sometimes they want it before they have the experience or knowledge to use it effectively.

A second approach to the problem is the self-amortizing investment. This procedure involves the establishment of enterprises in the LDC's by foreign investors; over a period of years these enterprises are sold to local investors or become the property of local government organizations. Several plans along these lines have been worked out in some detail by Aaron Scheinfeld, chairman of the board of Manpower, Inc., of Milwaukee.

Other proposals with the same purpose include a plan to create a federally chartered corporation to promote investments in LDC's. To be known as U.S. Overseas Private Investment Corporation, it would receive the cooperation of U.S. AID in securing insurance against confiscation or restrictions on the convertibility of funds. This organization would hope to tap an estimated $1.5 billion in U.S. capital, which would be available if adequate insurance could be guaranteed.

So far, this book has dealt essentially with U.S. public and private sector aid and investment because this country is by far the largest source of both. But aid programs of major importance are carried on by other nations such as the United Kingdom, Japan, West Germany, France, Sweden, Belgium, and Holland. They are the sources of substantial private investments in the food and other industries of the LDC's. Governmental aid from these countries usually flows to the former colonies of each: French aid to the former French West Africa, Cambodia, and Madagascar; British aid to East Africa, Nigeria, and its various former colonies in Southeast Asia. The Dutch have extended aid to Indonesia; the Belgians to the Congo, and so on. The West Germans and the Swedes have few recognizable former colonies, so they put both their aid and their investments where they think they will do the most good. The Portuguese, though painfully poor themselves, have put major efforts into their "overseas provinces" of Mozambique and Angola. The Japanese have paid more than $1 billion in reparations to various countries in Southeast Asia that they exploited during the short-lived Greater East Asia Co-Prosperity Sphere during World War II. Having paid off nearly all the reparations, they are continuing capital flows of some half-billion dollars annually as direct investments in western Australian ore projects and assorted other enterprises from the Philippines to India and Korea.

Finally, the Soviet bloc must be mentioned. Although they have political motives (as do most countries that give aid), and although their use of LDC citizens sent for training in Socialist countries and of Soviet personnel engaged in assorted projects outside the U.S.S.R. is fairly well documented, it is still a fact that the Soviet Union and Communist China have spent perhaps $3 billion on aid and projects in recent years. Projects have been as diverse as Egypt's Aswan High Dam, flour mills in Afghanistan, rural roads in Cambodia, and sugar-harvesting machinery for Cuba. Mainland Chinese aid emissaries have helped construct a modest forest-products complex in Nepal and a tobacco processing plant in Afghanistan, as well as roads and a port in Yemen.

12 Tomorrow

A NUMBER OF authoritative organizations and highly qualified individuals have tried to estimate mankind's food requirements for the remaining years of this century and to speculate on how these needs might be met.

Nearly all agree that during the years immediately ahead, most of the world's people will continue to meet their food needs with grain—wheat, rice, potatoes, pulses, oats, barley, corn—and with the meat, milk, and eggs obtained by feeding these grains to domesticated animals and birds. Increasingly, cereals will be fortified with protein concentrates, vitamins, and minerals, adding substantially to their nutritional value. In addition, consumption of fruits and vegetables will continue, and consumption of fish will increase.

Other foods, synthetics, and the products of sea farming

currently are available in small quantities and will become important a generation from now. Their cost is so prohibitive, however, that they will remain relatively unimportant for the rest of this century. Indeed, for nearly half the human race, even meat and dairy products are too expensive to be eaten in appreciable quantities.

The new varieties of grains, the fertilizers, the pesticides, and the water resources already known and exploitable are thought by some experts sufficient to produce the food needed between now and the end of the century. Similarly, the techniques of transport, storage, processing, packaging and distribution now in common practice in the developed countries are adequate to move the food from the farms into the mouths of the hungry. Also important are the advertising and merchandizing techniques now being used in the developed countries. If properly directed, these can persuade the hungry billions in the LDC's to eat the foods they need—fortified flours and protein beverages— and to abandon traditional taboos if these conflict with nutrition.

The Experts Speak

Let us look at some specific expressions regarding the outlook for the future:

Oxford Economist Colin Clark points out that, "If all the arable land in the world were farmed as efficiently as the Dutch farm their land, our earth could support a population of 28 billion."

Herman Kahn of the Hudson Institute in New York estimates that "with proper mechanization and fertilization, our present acreage could support six billion people, while the sea could yield from four to 40 times our present catch without upsetting the ecological balance."

Agriculture expert Lester Brown, writing in *Foreign Affairs* for October, 1968, points out that in India, although 4.2 million men have been sterilized and 2.4 million women protected with intrauterine contraceptive devices, and the birth rate has begun to decline, the population growth rate is still rising. Nevertheless, food production in 1968 increased spectacularly, and it has begun to look as though the food problem could be solved—even in India. Some farmers are becoming affluent. Land prices have risen as much as 600 per cent. Some urbanites are returning to their villages, where farmers now earn as much as $1,300 a year—twice a clerk's wage.

Former Secretary of Agriculture Orville Freeman feels that the momentum of current increases in food production in the LDC's could be maintained if 1.5 per cent of the GNP of the U.S. were committed for ten years with emphasis on technical assistance in food production. Freeman also suggested that the U.S. urge other developed countries to do the same. (This figure is higher than the 1 per cent of the GNP suggested by British economist Barbara Ward. Andrei Sakharov of the Soviet Academy of Sciences sets targets far higher—at nearly 15 per cent.)

At the November 1968 American Assembly meeting, one expert pointed out that man's progress has been notable. "Between 10 A.D. and 1846 A.D. there were 200 famines in the British Isles. Between 108 B.C. and 1911

A.D. there were 1,828 in China. Our day is nearly unique in that we have had no *major* famines since the Bengal Famine in 1948."

The experts attending this Assembly tried to estimate the world's needs in precise terms. Their conclusions were:

1. Worldwide food production *must* increase more rapidly than population growth because people are demanding more expensive foods—meat and dairy products.

2. World population is now growing by about 2.2 per cent a year, but the increase in the demand for food will be about 4 per cent a year.

3. Since food production is only part, though an important part, of general economic growth, to achieve the 4 per cent food production growth will require a 5 per cent GNP growth rate.

4. The present GNP for all the LDC's is about $200 billion. Given an average capital output ratio of 3:1, a $10 billion annual GNP growth would require investments of $30 billion a year.

5. One can hope that two-thirds of this—about $20 billion—will come from the LDC's themselves in soft currency. This means that $10 billion must come from the developed countries.

6. If contributions were made in proportion to GNP, the U.S. would have to provide about 40 per cent, or $4 billion of the required amount.

7. Hopefully one-quarter of this could come from the U.S. private sector, leaving $3 billion to come from

the public sector. This is twice what was appropriated in 1968.

8. The Assembly therefore recommended that U.S. aid to LDC's be increased forthwith to $3 billion a year.

The consensus of the group was that these objectives could be achieved, although the 4 per cent annual growth in food production is twice the U.S. average over the past 50 years, and a number of 1969 tax cuts may make it necessary to cut down on foreign aid.

Less optimistic was Britain's C. P. Snow. His gloomy outlook was based more on economic and psychological considerations and on the growing gap between the rich and the poor nations, than on technical possibilities. He predicted massive famines soon *unless:*

1. A concerted effort is made by the rich nations to help the poor.

2. An effort by the poor nations revolutionizes their food production.

3. A reduction of world population growth is achieved.

To achieve these objectives, Lord Snow thinks the developed nations would have to make available as much as 20 per cent of their GNP for 10 to 15 years, with concurrent drastic decreases in military spending. Indeed, this seems unlikely to be done.

Expectations in Grain

Specific projections of grain production, trade, and availability for the year 2000 for the world's large geographic areas were made by Don Paarlberg at the Assembly. He predicted that the U.S. and Canada, now producing 1,057 kilograms of grain per person per year, will increase yields enough to achieve a yearly per capita of 1,200 kilograms in the year 2000. The two countries also will nearly double their exports to 300 kilograms per person per year and will still have available 900 kilograms per person per year for their own consumption—a bit more than in 1968.

Latin America, because of its anticipated high population growth, will produce only 196 kilograms per person per year in the year 2000—down from 211, but increased imports will leave the Latin American people with the same per capita consumption they now have—207 kilograms per year to eat.

Western Europe, thanks to the application of new technology, will increase its per capita production by more than one-third to 420 kilograms per year, and with slightly increased imports, the Western Europeans will get 500 kilograms per year.

The Soviet Union and Eastern Europe will increase yearly production by some 15 per cent to 617 kilograms per person and will also increase imports enough to provide 625 kilograms per person per year—about halfway between Western Europe and North America.

Oceania will raise yields by nearly one-third, and exports by more than one-third, emerging in 2000 A.D. with a consumption level of only 310 kilograms per year.

Africa's per capita production will fall, and in spite of

doubled imports, it will have only its present inadequate 171 kilograms per person per year.

Paarlberg projects that Asia's production per person will also fall, and its imports will double, maintaining its present per capita level of consumption of 230 kilograms yearly.

According to these projections, North America and Oceania will emerge in 2000 as massive exporters of food to the rest of the world.

Who Will Pay?

But who will pay the bills? The President's Scientific Advisory Committee estimates that capital inputs in the LDC's between 1965 and 1985 will be required in the amount of:

$17 billion for production and distribution of fertilizer

$0.3 billion for seed

$1.9 billion for pesticides

$2 billion for farm machinery

This is quite apart from the complex of technical, educational, and other aid and entirely separate from the payment for the massive and continued grain imports from North America and Oceania.

By any measure, the LDC's will require grain and other inputs for which they will not be able to pay. Indeed, they will be fortunate if they are able to pay just the interest on their already immense debts to the developed countries. As a result, citizens of the granary nations will

have to pay the bills for the next few years if massive
starvation is to be avoided.

Where Will the Food Come From?

The staggering problem of payment aside for a moment, the technical problem of feeding the world's hungry
for the next few years is not unsolvable. We have examined the grain situation—the most important single issue.
There are other developments that may further increase
the availability of food for human beings:

More land can be utilized. Our planet has 32.9 billion
acres of land surface, of which 3.5 billion acres are classified as arable. But only 2.4 billion acres of this land are
planted in crops, leaving more than a billion acres unplanted.

Fortification of existing foods can greatly increase their
nutritional value. The cheapest protein fortifier now on
the horizon is spun protein made from soybeans. It can
be used to make a meat substitute equivalent to ham-
burger at half its cost. The most important amino acids
in which food grains are deficient—lysine, threonine, and
trytophan—can now be mass-produced for about $1.00 a
pound on a large scale. These are crystals, colorless, odor-
less, tasteless, and stable, and therefore ideal for use in
protein beverages such as Vitasoy or in fortifying flour
or other grain products. Wheat flour can now be enriched
with soybean protein concentrate for $2.00 a ton. Soon
proteins made from petroleum and coal, with the aid of
yeasts and algae, will be available at acceptable prices.

A second, somewhat more expensive, source of protein concentrate is fish meal, currently being produced in millions of tons and fed largely to animals. Peruvian fish meal costs $10 to $50 a ton and is 18 per cent protein, whereas soybean meal is 44 per cent protein and costs $72 a ton. For comparison, wheat is 8 per cent protein and costs $60 a ton.

The gradual replacement of draft animals, such as the ox or water buffalo, by internal combustion engines may cause problems during the years immediately ahead—until means are developed to transmit power economically from central nuclear or solar power installations to vehicles of local consumers. It will, however, save food, which could go to augment human diets.

Research now under way in the laboratories of universities, foundations, and private companies may bear fruit within the next few years. It is not known precisely what this fruit will be, but precedent promises high rewards.

The new emphasis on investments in LDC's, and help to them by public institutions such as the World Bank, and by private enterprises may likewise show positive results in the near future.

It is to be hoped that governments, particularly the U.S. administration, realize that the presidential foreign investment guidelines and other measures calculated to improve the balance of payments discourage investments in the LDC's and in the food industry. New guidelines could rectify this shortcoming and encourage private-sector capital flows to the LDC's and food industries.

The increasing use of synthetic fibers and the consequent release of cotton and flax acreage and sheep-grazing land for growing crops will further contribute to the availability of food.

Finally, education may change attitudes toward specific foods. Inland Brazilians may begin to eat more fish, Moslems may learn to accept pork, and Hindus beef.

Much-Needed Adjusters

Critics and skeptics may ask whether all these positive factors will lead to imbalances among the LDC's—surpluses one year, deficits the next, imbalances of trade growing out of seasonal crop variation, and general disarray. Happily, several automatic adjusters in agriculture function well in the LDC's. One factor is that in a good year, more grain can be fed to livestock and human diets enriched with meat and eggs. If production is low the next year, men can eat their laying hens and resume eating grain without suffering nutritionally. Grain directly consumed feeds seven times as many people as that fed to animals and consumed in the form of meat, milk, and eggs.

A second adjuster for climatic and market fluctuations is varied cropping. When wheat prices fall, the alert farmer can plant rye, or sorghum, or soy beans. Rice and corn produce twice as many calories per acre as wheat; rye only half as much; carrots twice as much; beets and celery the same; tomatoes, lettuce, peas, asparagus, only

accomplished by distillation—boiling sea water, condensing its vapor in cooling coils, and thus leaving behind the salts and minerals that make sea water unsuitable for human consumption or irrigation.

The largest desalinization plant in the world is at Rosarito, in northwestern Mexico. The plant, which cost nearly $9 million, processes 7.5 million gallons a day at a cost of about 25 U.S. cents per thousand gallons. The source of energy is gas. Another plant is in operation in Kuwait on the Persian Gulf, where large quantities of gas are available and there is no other local source of water, since it never rains in that part of the Arabian Desert. This plant is less efficient than the one in Mexico, and the water costs about 70 U.S. cents per thousand gallons. Other water desalinization plants are currently in operation at the U.S. base at Guantánamo, Cuba, on the Dutch island of Aruba, and at Freeport, Grand Bahama. The water each produces is inexpensive enough to be satisfactory for domestic consumption—but not for irrigation, which measures required quantities of water in millions of acre feet. For economically viable irrigation, water must cost about one U.S. cent per thousand gallons or less. The Kuwaiti sheiks, however, sometimes water their gardens with desalinated sea water.

As installations become larger and more efficient, and as nuclear or solar energy replaces gas and petroleum, experts believe desalinated sea water will become available at acceptable prices. Within the next generation, it may become feasible to use it for irrigation, opening millions of now arid acres along the coasts of many continents: the western coast of the Americas from San Diego to Cape Horn and the coasts of the Persian Gulf and the Red Sea. Much of this land lies under the equatorial sun, and proper irrigation would make it fertile and productive, and would allow multi-cropping.

Sea Farming

Although man harvests more than 50 million tons of fish and shellfish every year, the real potential of marine plant life is nearly untapped. Sea farming is today at about the same level of development as was land farming when the first nomadic hunter planted a seed and tried to help it grow.

Thus far, little attempt has been made to select or breed species of marine plant life whose seeds, berries, leaves, or roots would be suitable for human consumption. There is every indication that such an effort would be rewarding. The continental shelves adjacent to U.S. shores comprise millions of square miles of water shallow enough to allow the sun's rays to penetrate and catalyze plant growth. Moreover, marine plants, like their land-based cousins, require water and assorted nutrients, many of which— nitrogen, potassium, and phosphorus compounds—are in the sea water. It is not surprising, therefore, that the experts estimate that the total agricultural potential of the oceans' continental shelves is not much less than that of the earth's entire land surface.

No one suggests this potential will be tapped within

the next few decades. But in the twenty-first century, it will constitute a massive new source of human food.

Weather Control

Modest attempts have been made in the United States, Europe, and the U.S.S.R. to influence weather by seeding clouds with dry ice or silver iodide crystals, or by bombarding saturated clouds with sonic booms. But so far, success has been meager. Some attempts to "make it rain" have been successful, but experts could not explain why. In short, weather control is still in its pre-infancy.

Within a generation the situation is likely to change radically. Organizations such as the Environmental Science Services Administration, the Bureau of Reclamation, and the American Meteorological Society, as well as sister organizations in other lands have called conferences, compared notes and papers, and reported substantial progress. The experts are confident that by the end of the century there will be a worldwide meteorological service armed with computers to keep track of temperatures and pressures around the globe. The service will be able to undertake such tasks as stopping the rain that falls fruitlessly on the Indian Ocean and directing that moisture to fall on the great Australian desert. Similar operations could make gardens of the now arid wastes of most of North Africa, Arabia, and central Asia.

Herman Kahn suggests the kind of multiple operations that lie ahead of us in this field. By the year 2000, he asserts, the U.S. will derive most of its power from a dozen huge nuclear power installations, each with a capacity of perhaps 60,000 megawatts* (the capacity of Grand Coulee Dam is 1,974 megawatts). One might be built on Mount Wilson, overlooking Los Angeles. The heat produced by its reactors would raise the inversion layer that hangs over the basin of Los Angeles to perhaps 19,000 feet. Not only would this eliminate the city's smog, but it would probably draw in a sea breeze at about 10,000 feet, bringing frequent rains so that the surrounding desert could be changed into excellent farmland.

Fungi and Algae

Fungi and algae present great possibilities as sources of human nutrition. Both are currently under careful study. Yeast fungi in particular offer numerous possibilities for future human consumption. Of the 37,500 kinds of fungi, about 2,000 are classified as edible, but only a few have been studied from the commercial point of view. The production efficiency is about 65 per cent in terms of the amount of protein obtained in relation to the quantity of carbohydrates put in by the substance on which it feeds. This is an exceptionally high degree of conversion efficiency (corresponding figures: pork chops, 20 per cent; milk, 15 per cent; beef, 4 per cent). Yeast strains may be selected for the production of protein, fats, or B-vitamins and can be so fed as to yield a maximum amount of any one of these constituents. By-products of certain industries

---

* One megawatt is equal to one million watts.

such as sugar, wood pulp, and paper are carbohydrate-rich and can be used to produce large quantities of edible yeast. Such food yeast currently is available and being used as human food on a small scale; however, the main reason for its inclusion in food mixtures so far is to provide certain vitamins, rather than protein or energy. It is limited also by the fact that it is not competitive in price with other available protein concentrates.

Unicellular green alga has received special attention because of the large sums that have been spent on experiments to determine its potential as a food source on prolonged space voyages. A number of factors limit its possibilities for commercial use, however. Continuous cooling, removal of full-grown cells, and harvesting by filtering at regular intervals total a larger energy input than the energy output in the form of final algal products. The diffuse aggregate of tiny plants and animals found in the sea is known collectively as plankton. The Japanese have utilized krill, the largest of the plankton animals, as a source of food by pickling it in soy sauce and sugar and selling it on domestic markets. Research is being conducted with large quantities of a freshwater plankton, but so far it has proved indigestible and its taste disagreeable.

Photosynthesis

Photosynthesis is the process by which the sun's rays help the oxygen, hydrogen, carbon, and nitrogen in the air and water to combine into living cells and tissues.

So far, man has not learned to do this, although we can

use the products of ancient natural photosynthesis—fossil fuels—to make protein. We are learning to synthesize vitamins and some amino acids. But if we really learn photosynthesis—perhaps a generation or two hence—it will make possible the laboratory-factory that eventually may obviate traditional agriculture entirely, except as a hobby.

Among the many organizations currently working on this problem is the Thompson, Ramo, Wooldridge laboratory at Redondo Beach, California. Using electro-chemical energy instead of sunshine, these scientists claim to have achieved at least the first step in photo-synthesis.

Colonization

Finally, and most esoteric, other worlds already beckon us. If progress in space research in the next half-century continues at the rate set in the past decade, extra-terrestrial colonization will be the subject of serious conversation for our great-grandchildren.

We Need Not Starve

In a few short millennia human beings have learned to dominate most of their natural enemies and to make the planet's resources support a large and rapidly growing number of people. We have gone far in analyzing the nature of our physical environment and in learning to modify it to suit our convenience as well as our necessity, and, we have begun active exploration of our solar system.

Although we have not succeeded in ordering the affairs of men on earth to assure equity and stability, we have made progress in studying the problem. Theoretically, we now know how to contain our procreativity within the framework of our productivity, and to assure men everywhere not only of food, but also of leisure and the facilities to learn to understand and enjoy life.

But will men do it? Will attitudes and economics allow this knowledge to be utilized? The evidence at this point is not encouraging.

Given the average worldwide capital-output ratio of recent years, the world's people should now be investing in the world's economy at least 16 per cent of the gross product in order to realize a 4 per cent annual increase of over-all production. Such an increase is needed to raise by an appreciable measure the per capita consumption of man. We are failing to do so. The U.S. is now investing annually only about 10 per cent of its GNP. The richest large nation in the world is not responding to the requirements of world development. Other nations are falling even further short.

But man need not starve. We have the *means* to feed ourselves well into the next century. Hunger is not an isolated phenomenon. The food problem is one aspect of the more general problem of managing an economy. Barring unusual circumstances, people do not starve because of an absolute shortage of food, but because of poor management.

In the drought-plagued northeastern Brazilian village

of Patos there were tons of food in the marketplace, although much of the population did not have the money to buy it. In Trivandrum, in Calcutta, food was being freely bought, although scarcity had raised its price to two or three times the rationed price.

To the hungry world, the distinction between the unavailability of food and the inability to buy it is illusive. But the distinction is real. Man must recognize this distinction and rise to the challenge.

Appendix

APPENDIX I

Twenty Centuries of World Population Growth

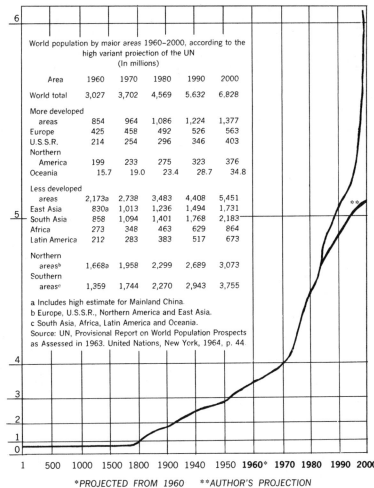

World population by major areas 1960–2000, according to the high variant projection of the UN
(In millions)

Area	1960	1970	1980	1990	2000
World total	3,027	3,702	4,569	5,632	6,828
More developed areas	854	964	1,086	1,224	1,377
Europe	425	458	492	526	563
U.S.S.R.	214	254	296	346	403
Northern America	199	233	275	323	376
Oceania	15.7	19.0	23.4	28.7	34.8
Less developed areas	2,173a	2,738	3,483	4,408	5,451
East Asia	830a	1,013	1,236	1,494	1,731
South Asia	858	1,094	1,401	1,768	2,183
Africa	273	348	463	629	864
Latin America	212	283	383	517	673
Northern areasb	1,668a	1,958	2,299	2,689	3,073
Southern areasc	1,359	1,744	2,270	2,943	3,755

a Includes high estimate for Mainland China.
b Europe, U.S.S.R., Northern America and East Asia.
c South Asia, Africa, Latin America and Oceania.
Source: UN, Provisional Report on World Population Prospects as Assessed in 1963. United Nations, New York, 1964, p. 44

BILLION PERSONS

1 500 1000 1500 1800 1900 1940 1950 **1960* 1970 1980 1990 2000**

*PROJECTED FROM 1960   **AUTHOR'S PROJECTION

BASED on DEPARTMENT of AGRICULTURE DATA   MODIFIED LOGARITHMIC SCALES

APPENDIX II

World* and regional agricultural production in relation to population

Indices, average 1952-56 = 100

	Average 1948-52	1953	1954	1955	1956	1957	1958	1959	1960	1961	1962	1963	1964	1965	1966	1967 (Preliminary)
TOTAL PRODUCTION																
ALL AGRICULTURAL PRODUCTS																
Western Europe	84	101	101	102	103	106	109	112	119	118	126	128	129	130	133	141
Eastern Europe and U.S.S.R.	82	94	96	105	115	118	128	130	132	135	138	133	145	148	165	164
North America	93	99	97	101	103	98	106	107	110	109	112	119	117	119	120	122
Oceania	90	97	97	104	106	102	117	119	123	125	133	137	142	135	151	140
Four above regions	87	98	98	103	107	106	113	116	119	119	124	126	130	131	138	140
Latin America	88	95	100	103	107	111	119	118	121	128	131	133	135	141	140	145
Near East	84	99	98	100	110	115	119	123	124	124	136	140	143	146	149	154
Far East*	87	97	100	104	107	108	112	117	121	126	129	131	135	133	135	143
Africa	86	97	101	102	107	107	110	115	122	119	127	131	134	135	135	143
Four above regions	87	97	100	103	108	110	114	118	122	125	130	133	136	137	138	145
ALL ABOVE REGIONS	87	98	99	103	107	107	114	117	120	121	126	129	132	133	138	142
FOOD PRODUCTS ONLY																
Western Europe	84	101	101	102	103	106	110	113	119	119	126	128	129	130	133	142
Eastern Europe and U.S.S.R.	83	94	96	104	114	118	129	131	133	137	140	134	146	149	167	165
North America	92	98	97	101	104	101	109	109	111	110	114	121	120	122	127	130
Oceania	92	100	98	104	101	99	117	115	123	123	135	138	145	137	158	140
Four above regions	87	98	98	103	107	107	115	117	120	121	126	127	131	132	141	144
Latin America	88	95	100	102	109	112	117	116	118	125	126	132	137	140	141	148
Near East	84	100	98	100	110	115	119	122	123	124	134	138	139	141	145	151
Far East*	87	98	100	104	107	108	113	118	123	127	129	132	136	134	135	144
Africa	87	98	102	101	106	106	108	113	120	117	124	128	130	130	130	138
Four above regions	87	98	100	103	108	109	114	117	121	124	128	132	136	136	137	145
ALL ABOVE REGIONS	87	98	99	103	107	108	115	117	121	122	126	129	133	134	140	144

* EXCLUDES MAINLAND CHINA.

APPENDIX III
The Changing Pattern of World Grain Trade
(net trade by regions)
1934–38

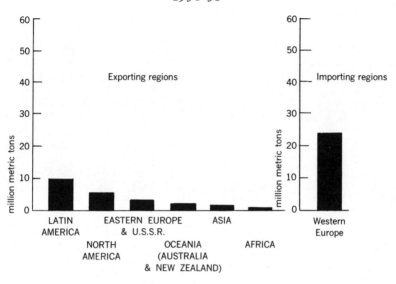

1966

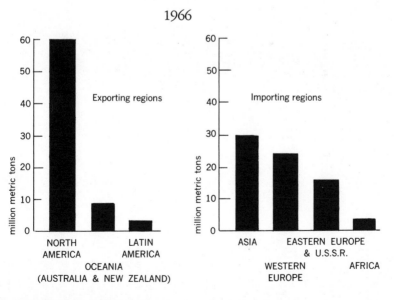

Bibliography and Recommended Reading List

Selected books for recommended reading are indicated by an asterisk*

*Brown, Lester, *Increasing World Food Output*, U.S. Department of Agriculture, April 1965.
A basic and clearly presented analysis of the worldwide man-land-food relationship.

Brown, Lester, *Man, Land and Food*, U.S. Department of Agriculture, November 1963.

*Brown, Lester, "The Agricultural Revolution in Asia" *Foreign Affairs*, July 1968.
An updated analysis of more recent trends in the man-land-food relationship with more optimistic conclusions.

*Carson, Rachel, *Silent Spring*, Fawcett Publication, Inc., Greenwich, Connecticut, 1962.
Winner of eight awards, including the Schweitzer Medal, this bestseller presents a shocking portrait of earth as a planet increasingly contaminated by man's carelessness with pesticides and insecticides.

Culliton, Barbara, "Wheat and Revolution," *Science News*, July 6, 1968.

Dema, J. S., *Nutrition in Relation to Agricultural Production*, FAO, Rome, 1965.

Department of State, Agency for International Development, *War on Hunger*, September 1968.

Erlich, Paul, *The Population Bomb*, Ballantyne Books, Inc., New York 1968.

173

Food and Agriculture Organization, *The State of Food and Agriculture,*
1967, Rome.

*Food and Agriculture Organization, *The State of Food and Agriculture,*
1968, Rome.
A comprehensive world review and outlook based on statistics
available to FAO up to July 15, 1968. Includes sections on raising
agricultural productivity in developing countries through techno-
logical improvement and on improved storage and its contribution
to world food supplies.

Food and Agriculture Organization, *World Review of Animal Production,*
1967.

Freeman, Orville, *World without Hunger,* Frederick A. Praeger, 1968.

*Myrdal, Gunnar, *Asian Drama: An Inquiry into the Poverty of Nations,*
Pantheon, 1968.
Takes up the facts of economy in South Asian countries and con-
cludes that national economic planning is useless in these nations
—largely because of human frailty, poor resources, debilitating
climates.

*Hardin, Clifford, editor, *Overcoming World Hunger,* The American Assembly, Columbia University, Prentice Hall, 1969.
Originally designed as background reading for participants in the
American Assembly conference on overcoming world hunger, the
book includes timely articles by experts on population growth and
control, nutrition, agricultural technology, foreign aid, and other
pertinent topics.

Kaiser Aluminum News, Volume 26, Numbers 1 and 2.

Oberg, Sven, editor, Alfa-Laval International, 1967/1968, Tumba,
Sweden.

Paddock, William and Paul, *Famine 1975! America's Decision: Who Will
Survive?,* Little, Brown, Boston 1967.

Scott, John, *Hunger—Must We Starve?,* Time Inc., 1966.

Ward, Barbara, *The Lopsided World,* W. W. Norton & Company, Inc.,
New York, 1968.

The World Food Problem, A Report of the President's Science Advisory
Committee, May 1967.

Index

Photo Credits

We wish to thank the following photo services and distributors, as well as the individual photographers (whose names appear in parentheses), for the use of photographs in this book.

THE UNDERNOURISHED
Biafra Relief Services Foundation, New York City:
2
Life Picture Collection, Time-Life Inc., New York City:
1 (Robert Mottar), 3 (Robert Mottar)

THE NECESSARY BALANCE—
SOIL AND WATER
Black Star, New York City:
6 (Anthony Howarth),
17 (Dr. Georg Gerster), 18 (Cyenet)
Food and Agriculture Organization:
4, 8 (Emmet Bright),
12 (T. S. Satyan), 15
Philip Gendreau, New York City:
7, 9–11, 13, 14, 16, 19
United Nations, New York City:
5

REVITALIZING THE SOIL—
FERTILIZER
Philip Gendreau:
20, 21

THE CORN STORY
Food and Agriculture Organization:
23 (P. Johnson), 24 (Emmet Bright),
27 (S. Theuvenet), 28 (F. Botts)
Philip Gendreau:
22, 25, 26, 29, 30

WHAT PRICE, RICE?
Black Star:
35 (Francois Sully)
Food and Agriculture Organization:
37 (V. U. Contino)
Philip Gendreau:
36, 38–41
The Rockefeller Foundation, New York City:
31–33
United States Department of Agriculture, Washington, D.C.:
34

THE WONDER OF WHEAT
Black Star:
49 (John Launois), 52 (Bill Witt)
Food and Agriculture Organization:
43, 44 (S. Larrain), 51 (B. Bhansali)
Philip Gendreau:
45, 48, 50

United States Department of Agriculture:
42

COMBATTING PESTS
Food and Agriculture Organization:
53 (P. Keen), 54 (Jean Manuel),
56, 58 (S. Larrain)
Philip Gendreau:
55, 57 (Ralph Hancock)
Wide World Photos (Associated Press), New York City:
60

MANY WAYS TO NET A CATCH
Black Star:
66 (Hans Hubmann),
75 (Herbert Lanks)
Food Agriculture Organization:
62 (A. Defever), 63 (S. Larrain),
65 (S. Larrain)
Philip Gendreau:
55, 57 (Ralph Hancock)
United Nations:
69, 70
United Press International, New York City:
72, 73

BREAD—THE BASIS
Black Star:
76 (Franke Keating), 79 (Jean Lyn),
83 (Louis O. Williams),
84 (Hans Hubmann)
Philip Gendreau:
77, 78, 80, 81, 82 (Ray Garner), 85, 86

FOOD AROUND THE WORLD
Biafra Relief Services Foundation:
99
Black Star:
90 (Bernhard Moosbrugger),
93 (Middle East Features),
95 (Hans Gabathuler),
98 (A. Da Cruz), 100 (John Launois),
104 (Frances Ceman),
106 (Nona and Peter Gordon),
117 (F. Jacobs)
Philip Gendreau:
87, 88 (William LaVarre), 89, 91, 92, 94,
96, 97, 101, 102, 103, 105, 107,
108 (J. W. McManigal), 109–112, 114–116
United Press International:
113